Welcome to Our World

A collection of life writing

by people living with dementia

Edited by Liz Jennings

Published in 2014 by Forget-Me-Nots, Canterbury

Made and printed by NXP Europe, Tunbridge Wells

ISBN 978-0-9930742-0-2

Acknowledgements

This project has been a real team effort and we would wish to express our sincerest thanks to...

First and foremost to our husbands, wives, families, loved ones and dear friends, whose love and support is so crucial to us.

To Keith Oliver for his vision and drive to see the project through from an idea to a reality and for his enthusiasm *en route*.

To Liz Jennings for her outstanding teaching which, like all gifted teachers, embraced the thoughtful planning, stimulating ideas, patience and encouragement which guided us to becoming writers.

To Alex, Charley, Jennie, Sophie and Lewis, the psychology students who became our dear friends. Without your skills, patience and maturity - which belied your age - the project would never have succeeded.

To Rachael Litherland at DEEP (Dementia Engagement and Empowerment Project), and Tim Beanland, Janet Baylis and Katie Bennett at The Alzheimer's Society, for believing in us and sharing the vision enough to give us funding so it could become a reality.

To Lloyds Banking Group for supporting the development of Welcome to our World, through funding the Alzheimer's Society Innovation Fund 2014/15.

To Daren Kearl, Community Development Librarian at the Beaney House of Art and Knowledge, for all your help and support in providing us with such a comfortable home base in the Beaney, where we all felt so relaxed and able to concentrate on our writing.

To April Doyle, tutor and administrator for Community Adult Education at Canterbury Christ Church University, and Elizabeth Field of Kent and Medway NHS Social Partnership Trust, for joining our editorial team and bringing your wisdom and advice which helped so much in moving towards this finished book.

To John Neal and Bob Walker for your genuine interest and supportive comments connected to the 'You and Yours' BBC Radio 4 programme.

Once again, a BIG thank you, from

The authors:

A. Charles, B. de Fréne, Chris N, Chris R, Keith, M. J. Saints, Rose, Tony

Contents

Foreword from Jo Brand   7

Preface from Keith Oliver   9

Foreword from the students   11

Introduction from Liz Jennings   15

The Writing:

A. Charles   23

B. de Fréne   57

Chris N   71

Chris R   97

Keith   125

M. J. Saints   175

Rose   189

Tony   211

The Maidstone Conference Talk   243

After the course...   253

Some life writing exercises to try   254

Useful web addresses   256

Foreword from Jo Brand

When thinking about how to introduce this book, it reminded me of how I first came face to face with Alzheimer's when I was a psychiatric nurse. On the one hand, dementia is a tragic and debilitating condition in which beloved relatives are lost to the rest of their families as they have known them, but on the other hand, the contributors to this book seem to be so pragmatic, joyful and positive that it is hard not to be swept along by their enthusiasm.

I suppose my first encounter with people experiencing the effects of Alzheimer's was on a ward for the elderly at the Bethlem Royal Hospital in Kent. This was only my second placement and I was still slightly naïve and shy... certainly not the gobby old boot I am today.

I found it a difficult placement, I suppose because it made me so sad... all those people, mostly women, who seemed mere child-like husks of their former selves. These were the days when the medical model reigned supreme, though, and little attention was paid to the social, emotional and interactive side of our little group's lives.

I particularly remember that a new drug was being trialled and had the unfortunate side-effect of making everyone who took it smell like gone-off fish. *Bloody Hell,* I remember thinking to myself... *As if their lives aren't dreadful enough already and now look... a further reason for people to keep their distance.*

Well, things have changed since then, and we have charities like the Alzheimer's Society that actually do campaigning work trying to change peoples' lives.

These days, those with a foot already in the camp of Alzheimer's have joined the fight to improve the lives of those living with dementia, and are working from the inside with their unique perspective to offer an invaluable insight into the experience of those who used to disappear into themselves never to be seen again.

I take my hat off to all the contributors to this book. It's touching and funny... and why not use humour in what many perceive to be the darkest of situations? For me, it's always been a foolproof way of dragging people out of the Slough of Despond. (I am quoting The Pilgrim's Progress there, not slagging off Slough).

Old age is coming to all of us and Alzheimer's to some of us. Here's a book that shines a little light.

Jo Brand
Alzheimer's Society Ambassador

Preface by Keith Oliver

It's a rare moment when a wide range of positive elements come together, gel, harmonise and contribute to as successful a piece of work as the one I hope you are about to engage with.

This is not just another book about dementia: what makes this book unique is that it is written by a group of people who each have a diagnosis of dementia, who want to share some stories from their lives alongside expressing some thoughts surrounding inhabiting the world of dementia from the inside.

The project grew from a seed of an idea which was planted and nurtured around a year ago, as I write, when, during a Life Writing course at Canterbury Christ Church University, I was encouraged by fellow students and April, our tutor on that course, to consider putting some thoughts and ideas into a book.

I briefly considered writing my own memoirs, but felt this was too solitary an exercise, and that few people would want to hear just my story. I love being part of a team and sharing ideas and aspirations with others. Quickly, I realised when talking to fellow members of our Kent Forget-Me-Nots, a group of people with dementia, that others liked the idea of being encouraged to write about our past and our present.

Soon afterwards, the Dementia Engagement and Empowerment Project (DEEP), supported us with a grant for a tutor and refreshments to assist our writing sessions, and Daren Kearl, Canterbury's Community Development Librarian, had offered us a room in The Beaney, in which to meet and write. A further grant from Lloyd's Bank, via the Alzheimer's Society has enabled us to cover the cost of moving from the writing course to this book.

I suspect some pieces of writing will make you smile and hopefully laugh out loud, some will provoke thoughts and take you to familiar and new places in your deepest consciousness, whilst others may well bring a lump to your throat.

We are a diverse group of people - many of us have never written anything beyond letters and emails before - so this was an exciting challenge for us. It is a real privilege to introduce this book to you, and I hope that you feel uplifted by the experience of sharing some of our memories with us. Now that the project is complete and the book is a reality, perhaps it is right to take the time out to go and smell the roses, which are in full bloom as I write.

Thank you,

Keith Oliver, Kent and Medway NHS Partnership Trust Dementia Service User Envoy

Canterbury, October 2014

Preface by the Psychology Students

The old view of dementia as a condition which immediately disqualifies a person from productive activity and personal and social development is, thankfully, being challenged, and the following pages represent one of the greatest challenges to this view. At the time of writing, it is the first book of its kind; a book written by people living with dementia in a social context, sharing stories and reminiscing about life, discussing what makes each person unique, and turning all of this into a book.

From our perspectives as undergraduate psychology students, working with the authors as a group and individually to support writing, seeing first-hand how this project work and being a part of it has been truly inspiring.

The medical definition of dementia tells us that it is 'degenerative'; that cognitive and social function diminishes over time.

This seems in direct contradiction to our own experience.

Over the course of the sessions we saw people, some initially sceptical about their own writing skills, become increasingly confident, coming into their own, sharing more of their experiences and bonding as a group. It was clear that the group sessions, in which people were supported in their writing and being allowed to get into their own stories in a social context, were hugely important in determining the quality of the final product, and in determining the meaning the project had for individuals.

The project also had meaning for us as students. While it was satisfying to be a part of something that we felt was hugely important and beneficial, on another level it was a pleasure to be allowed into peoples' lives and to hear their stories, and get to know them better as individuals and as a group. Working with people, and using different creative methods to inspire people to write, dictate or simply reminisce about influential moments in their lives, was both challenging and exciting for us as students in the field of psychology.

While we were supporting people to enable expression of their life stories, we found ourselves being supported by them. We were not simply learning about their lives, but also about our own, gaining an inter-generational perspective on the challenges that life presents, and on the strength we possess to face these challenges, as individuals and as a community.

We have gained a greater understanding of the tragedies, comedies, loves and losses that make up the tapestry of human experience, and have done so from people with lived experience, rather than from the text book or from the lecture theatre. It is these lived experiences that, for us, make psychology such a fascinating subject.

As the project drew towards its conclusion, we felt it was a shame that, as with all good things, the end was inevitable. However, we are proud to have been a part of it, and we shall not soon forget the time we spent with this amazing group of people. We will always be inspired by them and the funny, heart-warming, touching, witty and fascinating stories that we have heard, and that have been included in the following pages.

Whether you are a person with dementia, or know a person with dementia, or whether you are simply interested in getting to know the people behind this work, we hope that you will find the same inspiration and joy reading these pages as we did helping to put them together.

Thank you,

Alex Bone, Charley Massingham, Sophie Razzel, Jennie Russell, Lewis Slade

Introduction by Liz Jennings, course tutor

This is not so much an introduction as an invitation.

In these pages, you're going to meet some wonderful people, with some fascinating stories to tell you about their lives and experience. Meeting them and getting to know each writer's 'voice' has been thrilling for me.

A. Charles' experiences opened our eyes to a life bursting at the seams with travel and adventure, all of which he shared with grace, humour and humility. If you need a plan, he's your man.

B. de Fréne had us all on the edge of our seats regularly, and listening to her pieces was always exciting. Her strong opinions and clear instinct for narrative send off sparks: when she lifts a pen, it's like she's picking up a blowtorch.

Chris N delighted us all, again and again. With his eye for finding the funny in any situation, his writing makes me wish I'd been there with him, able to share the joy he finds in the bizarre moments of everyday life.

Chris R, who wasn't sure if writing was his thing... Ha! From the moment he put pen to paper, he brought poetry to the group, putting words down with a natural rhythm, balance, and humour that gave the simplest sentence a craftsman's beauty.

Keith's determination and drive was matched perfectly by his willingness to be open and honest. His vulnerability gave his writing strength and integrity, always shaped by kindness. He writes, as he lives, with great generosity and warmth.

M. J. Saints brought a ray of sunshine to our meetings:

indeed, she carries one with her wherever she goes. Her pieces, imbued with such wistfulness and sensitivity, as well as the gentlest, most delightful humour, meant there was never a dry eye in the room when she read her work to us.

Rose's writing revealed the tender heart of one who cares deeply for her family, and who has dedicated herself to doing a good job of raising her daughters, all over the world. Her ability to count her blessings will uplift you as you read her work.

Tony has a storyteller's eye for detail and intrigue, and, like all good carpenters, he has the ability to hit the nail on the head! His clear, direct prose appears effortless, while conveying deep and complex thoughts and feelings, as well as simple truths.

When I first met these writers, I had only the most basic understanding of dementia. I approached the group as I did other writing groups I'd led - as an interesting bunch of new people to meet, with their own passions and motivations, ups and downs, and things to say.

As we progressed, I felt I must improve my understanding of dementia, so I started reading as much as I could about it. But, as I began researching, I felt my confidence wane; my naivety suddenly seemed so embarrassing: what did I think I was doing? I became horribly aware of my lack of qualifications and experience: I never feel like a 'proper' writer as it is, (heck, half the time I don't feel like a 'proper grown-up'!) This time, though, I was really out of my depth.

I spoke to Keith, voicing some of my fears and lack of faith in the exercises I had planned.

'Liz,' he said, looking at me very seriously, 'If you'd told me in advance half of the things you've had us doing, I'd have said *I don't think that'll work!* But I'd have been wrong: keep going, keep pushing us, keep trying new things - we'll take it moment by moment. The moment things don't work - change direction.'

And so the pattern was set. I kept suggesting crazy ideas: instant poetry which required mind-gymnastics; writing inspired by sights, sounds, smells... we wrote without knowing where it would take us.

And I stayed flexible. When things didn't click, I had to be creative, switching direction without fuss. The writers were gracious, and it seemed to work. I always felt so excited about our writing sessions, because, despite the plan, it was very much a moment-by-moment experience, with my antennae constantly alert, assessing the response of each writer.

Before I began editing this book, those involved in its creation agreed on a single house-style rule: I needed to ensure that, throughout all that follows, the word 'dementia' should appear with a small 'd'.

That says it all, to me. The people who I met with to write, whose stories are in these pages, are not defined by dementia.

They wrestle with it, they feel frustration with it at times, but they're also much bigger than it. They've lived, and continue to live, rich, meaningful lives. Their passions prevail - and develop. They're still changing and growing as people, taking on new skills and embracing new challenges with determination, humour and dignity.

Universal truths are captured within these pages. If you've ever loved, lost, hurt, laughed, wept, felt accepted or rejected, hoped, failed, succeeded or simply sighed at life as you watch it fly by, you'll find yourself relating to these eight wonderful writers.

This project has proved again and again that we none of us live or work in isolation, and there are those that I really must thank.

To Keith Oliver, the most tenacious person I've ever met: thank you for trusting me, and for being so kind. And to the seven other writers whose work is contained in this book, who accepted me so readily, who were so brave in writing and sharing their work, and who rose to every challenge I set before them with such willing courage - thank you.

To Alex, Charley, Jennie, Lewis, and Sophie, the psychology students who gave of themselves, and brought out the best in the writers with gentleness and understanding. It couldn't have happened without you, simple as that.

To Daren Kearl at the Beaney, who always did all he could - and then some - to support us.

To April Doyle, of Christ Church University, Canterbury, for her wisdom, humour, guidance and support through the publishing process.

To Dr. Elizabeth Field, the psychologist working with the Forget-Me-Nots group. Her insights, understanding and encouragement lifted me up and set me straight many times.

To Katy Hirst, of Bright Shadow, whose vast experience of working in creative arts with people with dementia made her a terrific sounding board, and whose encouragement never ceased.

To Mark, my husband, who shared my joy in the course as if it were his own, and to Isobel Peaty: where would we be without friends?

Lastly, to Maisie and Reuben, who are nine and six at the time of writing, and who so sweetly asked after the writers, by name, after each group session. You two constantly inspire me in my own writing. One day, I hope you'll try life writing - although I dread to think what you'll say...

Liz Jennings, September 2014

The Writing

A.Charles

To my wife Pauline, daughter Sarah,
family and friends

Writing in this section was supported by Charley

Teaching Spies in Wormwood Scrubs
and
My Call to the Bar

Prior to being called to the Bar, I decided to get a secondary qualification, in view of the state of uncertainty in industry in 1959. So I started a course reading for the Postgraduate Certificate in Education of the University of London at St. Mary's College, Strawberry Hill, Twickenham, now part of London University. In 1960 I obtained my Postgraduate Certificate in Education. This was vital in getting a post as a lecturer/instructor and Assistant Educational Psychologist at HM Prison, Wormwood Scrubs. This was intended to support me financially until my call to the Bar and so it was.

In the prison I took classes in English, Current Affairs, History, Constitutional Law, and Geography.

The prison was memorable in that it was a first offenders' prison, mainly peopled by convicted murderers and spies. Spies in my classes included Col. Lonsdale, the Russian KGB Officer, who was eventually exchanged for Gary Powers, the U2 pilot, and John Vassell, the Admiralty spy, and lastly George Blake, the double agent.

Blake was responsible for the deaths of many British agents. He confessed in 1961 to having passed Moscow copies of every important official document that he saw. I was so appalled by Blake's crimes that he must be the only person I have ever refused to shake hands with. He was sentenced to forty two years imprisonment. He was in my Current Affairs class. Then in 1966, by which time I had taken another job, he escaped over the wall into a waiting car and ending up in Moscow where he still is.

Most of my studying for my call to the Bar was done between and after the classes in the prison library in the local library at Hammersmith, and my flat near Barnes Common. I lectured for three years at Wormwood Scrubs.

In one of my classes I had a Middle Eastern murderer. After a while I had formed the impression that this man could not have murdered someone in the street and cut off his head. He was too pleasant and easy going a character. Then one day I just caught a glimpse of a look of malice and sheer evil towards a fellow prisoner, and instantly I changed my view. How wrong can one be in an assessment of a character! This was an important lesson for me to learn, both in later jobs and in the outside world, that has stayed with me.

Later I transferred to making assessments in a remand home for young criminals, where the lessons learned in Wormwood Scrubs were put into practice. Particularly, the lessons I had learnt as Assistant Educational Psychologist in the Scrubs were used.

Between 6pm and 7pm most evenings I returned to Wormwood Scrubs to lecture at evening classes. The young criminals in the remand centre were assessed for transfer to their next place of incarceration by me and reports were written by me for each person, usually during the class whilst the students were completing set exercises.

Having attended the required number of dinners at Gray's

Inn, one of the four Inns of Court, in 1963 I had the great pleasure of being called to the Bar as a barrister. I was presented with a book on *The Duty and Art in Advocacy* by the late Devlin J., Treasurer of Gray's Inn.

My speech that night at the Gray's Inn dinner was in Latin *Nunc in Lingua Latina...* Great fun! A colleague made his speech in Russian. It won't surprise the reader that neither of us was allowed by our colleagues to finish! I then became a member of the Bar Association of Commerce, Industry and Finance, and worked as a non-practising barrister in industry, as indeed did many others.

Expedition to Egypt

Life is not measured by the number of breaths we take but by the places and moments that take our breath away. Anonymous.

For me my expedition to Egypt in 1963 was one such place, and a series of such moments.

A group of my friends from various colleges met in an Oxford College common room. Having been called to the Bar in 1963, it was decided that I would drive with three friends to Piraeus, the port for Athens, and cross by boat to Alexandria where we were to be met by two South African friends with their Land Rover. I attended six illustrated lectures on the tomb of Tutankhamun: I had previously done preparatory work on Egyptology. The roads to Greece were fine to Thessaloniki and beyond to the Turkish border, after which there was just tracks to Istanbul.

I arranged to leave the car for a few months in Athens. We then joined our two South African colleagues with their Land Rover. The South Africans had erected a tough wire cage over the rear for security. We then sailed from Piraeus to Alexandria, passing Crete on a fine summer night. Our party had three people essential to our mission: an engineer, a doctor and an Egyptologist, (me).

From Alexandria we drove to Giza, just outside Cairo and camped in what used to be the grounds of King Farouk's palaces, with the pyramids showing up against the warm night sky. The next day we climbed up a rather tenuous route to the top of the

Great Pyramid of Cheops. We viewed the Giant Sphinx and rode on a camel, then set for Asyut, passing the Step Pyramid of Saqqara and a cluster of nine pyramids. Then there was the long drive to Asyut and on to Luxor. Karnak and Luxor are two of the most impressive temples in Egypt.

But the *pièce de résistance* was the Valley of the Kings and the Valley of the Queens on the West Bank of the Nile. We had to re-cross the Nile by ferry to get there, passing on the way the Colossi of Memnon. The Mortuary Temple of Queen Hatshepsut rises out of the Desert in a series of terraces that merge with the limestone cliffs. I deliberately investigated the Valley of the Kings on my own, staying there for half an hour, taking in the pervading atmosphere of this incredible place. One had to know what happened there to fully appreciate this valley.

We then drove a long distance to Aswan near the First Cataract. After the building of the High Dam (1960-1971), the monuments were relocated to a nearby island. At Aswan we did not camp for a change, but stayed at the Catholic Mission for a while in a big dormitory. We stayed so we could contact the Egyptian military who would appoint a compulsory guide to lead us over the stretch of the Sahara between Aswan and Abu Simbel and get a BBC film unit to join us. We talked animatedly far into the night with our fellow Egyptian army officers. A wonderful evening!

The next day I then decided we would drive the Land Rover around the Aswan Dam building works being carried out by the Soviets, utilising my Russian language learnt in the army. All fascinating! I was taught the Russian language by Princess Coe, a White Russian in York.

The Egyptian colonel arranged a Bedouin guide who knew the Sahara. We joined up with the BBC film unit in their Land Rover, who accompanied us over the next three days. The next day we passed a vast unexpected camel graveyard. I got a photo of this through the windscreen.

On the third day, we reached the impressive rock temples at Abu Simbel and façade of huge statues. We entered deep into the temples. The Great Temple is now at the foot of the new Lake Nasser. UNESCO had the temples cut from the hill and moved them to an artificial cliff well above their original position.

On the way back, we had the dreadful misfortune of knocking down and injuring a child in the village, who ran out without warning in front of our vehicle, in respect of which all seven of us were put in the village jail with a barred window overlooking the village square. I gave this cell the name 'Black Hole of Calcutta'. It was only weeks after the British invasion of Suez and this did not bode well. We spent the night on the floor. The next day we were suddenly released, apparently because of an urgent phone call from the UK Ambassador in Cairo, clearing us of any liability.

Apart from this terrible incident, wow, did I love, love, love this exciting and incredibly long holiday! The memories will remain with me forever. There were many good times before and after, but nothing quite like this.

Postscript

When I first met my future wife, Pauline Whitley, not long after my return from Egypt, at a fancy dress party in Chelsea I was wearing a fez and a white sheet and sandals! All of this must have gone down well for the rest of the story is history!

Being at the Salzburg Seminar

In 1967 I was elected a Fellow of the Salzburg Seminar in American Studies after a London interview. I was then asked to attend a month's session at the Schloss Leopoldskron which in my view had almost the status of a US overseas university, a beautiful venue. This was situated in a fine mansion on a lakeside outside Salzburg.

The session was entitled American Law and Legal Institutions and attended by many other Fellows from all over Europe, including three from Czechoslovakia. The Faculty Professors included Prof. Cardozo, one time Professor of Law at Cornell University, USA, and a US government consultant. This course was to add significantly to my First Class Certificate in Foreign Law and Comparative Law, 1965, at the City of London College (now London University).

I had the happy experience of meeting professional Europeans every day for a month, and made many friends. The beer cellar after each day's work was socially a marvellous place to have many a fascinating conversation, far into the evenings. Sitting beside the beautiful lake on a hot summer's day with such company was quite delightful and something I will always remember. It was here that I first became conscious of being noticeably less insular and more European.

A coach-load of us made a three-day visit to Prague, Czechoslovakia, three weeks before the Russian invasion. My three Czech colleagues did not accompany us.

I shall never forget the massive menacing towers at the frontier crossing with a steel barrier across the road from Austria. For the first time I experienced the horrific actuality of the Cold War. Steely eyes on each gruesome and menacing tower were trained on every move we made. This is something one had to experience to understand what had been going on in Czechoslovakia at that time. So began three incredible days, so close to Salzburg. Those three days will stay with me always.

We stayed at the Charles University in a large dormitory. I was woken up very early one morning by an immense clattering from the main road outside the University: a noise which I was quite convinced was being made by tanks, the sound of which I had got used to in my army days. If so, that could only be Russian tanks, as an invasion was half-expected.

I was mightily relieved when I eventually got to the window. It transpired that the noise was being caused by trams passing over sewers not far from the road surface!

That day we had people coming up to us, asking for help to escape to Austria. This got quite embarrassing and awful to have to refuse. Although Prague was a fine city, I was quite pleased to get back to the dreaded frontier post after three days. About three weeks later the Russian invasion actually started and the Russians took over the city.

Pauline and I went to Prague on a week's holiday much later, long after the Berlin Wall had fallen and the Russians had left, when I saw a very different city.

More recently the Salzburg Seminar became the Salzburg

Global Seminar and I and all the others became Fellows of the Salzburg Global Seminar, rather than Fellows of the Salzburg Seminar. Long may this splendid institution carry on its good work.

How I became involved in the African Law Reports

On my return from Salzburg, I had an interview with Dr. Alan Milner, a fellow of Trinity College, and formally Dean at Ahmadu Bello University in Nigeria. Alan told me that in addition to his fellowship at Trinity, he had started to produce the *African Law Reports*, with help from the Ford Foundation. Both Alan and I were both barristers at law at Gray's Inn.

As a result of the interview, Alan appointed me Commercial Series Editor of the *African Law Reports*. Another fellow barrister, Rupert Bursell, was one of my five Editorial Associates. Alan arranged that my family and I would live in a university block of flats occupied by visiting University Fellows.

My African Carvings and the Riot in Freetown

My native African carvings came from Freetown, the capital city of Sierra Leone. I have four of them.

When I look at my African carvings, I am reminded of the time I visited Freetown for one week; there was a riot at the time.

In May 1968 I flew out to Freetown, capital of Sierra Leone, by way of The Gambia, West Africa, before landing at the airport for Freetown. I had the misfortune of arriving in Freetown in the midst of an uprising.

Our coach weaved its way through a vast crowd of people, marching army officers and senior NCOs (Non-Commissioned Officers) in chains down the main road.

I saw the riot for only about five minutes. I saw more of the results of it, but it lives on in one's mind that sort of thing. One does not expect to see it, a public riot against the army. I did not know what to expect, after all I wasn't in my own country and it was my first time in Africa. I was the only English person there and everyone looked at me thinking 'who are you?' I did not go out much after that. Some start to my trip! Eventually, I managed to get to the paramount hotel overlooking Freetown Bay.

I was in Freetown for a week. One of the purposes of the visit was to inspect old law manuscripts, only I quickly discovered they had all been eaten by termites!

I met the Hon. Sir Samuel Bankole Jones, President of the Court of Appeal for Sierra Leone, who sent a car round to my hotel for me, and we talked for a long time in his house. He told me that his wife had had to get him out of his house in the boot of his car during the riots. Later that week he took me on several trips to the coast.

After a wonderful week, I flew back to the UK and Oxford, loaded with African bits and pieces, all of which I still have - a drum, a spear, horns, four African wooden heads, amongst other things - all displayed in front of my *African Law Reports* and shown on the photo, a permanent reminder of those wonderful days in West Africa.

When I got back to the UK after one week, as there was only one plane per week, I responded to a fascinating job advertisement, for a legal job in Brussels. I was chosen for this job for Clark Equipment Company of the USA.

I remember the second part of my interview as it was in a

nightclub where I ended up with an attractive hostess on my knee, and my reactions were watched with keen interest. I was a very good dancer at this time, I took to the floor with this lady and when I returned to my interviewers, I received a grand round of applause.

After being offered the job, I flew out to the mid-west of the US with my family and began my six months of training for the post in Brussels.

Living in America

I have chosen to write about a place where I was particularly happy, and made plenty of friends, many of whom inspired me. That place was the USA.

My wife and I and our two young children, Philip and Sarah, were given the use of a large house not far from the Clark Equipment Company's Headquarters, together with the largest car I have ever driven.

I was appointed UK Counsel and Assistant European Counsel to take effect when I had returned to Europe after my training in the USA. After three months my family and I opted to take over a large farm house with forty acres of forest in Barron Lake in Michigan to the great delight of Philip and Sarah.

We were invited to colleagues' houses and in return we entertained them. One fascinating invitation was to meet a considerable number of people who wanted to meet people from England. What fun!

There are many out of the way office visits for us, some business, and some social to Washington DC, New York, Detroit, Minneapolis, Chicago and London, Ontario.

We spent an amazing six months in this atmosphere before sailing to France on the QE2 and enjoying one hour longer each night, dancing. What an incredible six months' introduction to Clark Equipment Company. I cannot recall a more wonderful six months with such marvellous people.   Once we had arrived in France we drove to Brussels, and more wonderful experiences.

When working in Brussels, part of my job was to fly to the UK and back on the company plane every two weeks and I stayed in the company flat in Mayfair during my time in the UK. I made many interesting visits to the UK Company in Camberley where I worked with the Managing Director and the Industrial Relations Manager. I gave lectures to the employees, as there was much new employment statute law in the UK at the time. Thanks to the company plane, other parts of the country were also visited.

Lectures were also given to senior employees on the Treaty of Rome, 1957, which established the Common Market. In Brussels I was only the second ever British barrister, although there may have been a British Solicitor. In my final years there I undertook EEC translation work from French to English and English to French with my wife.

South India, 2004

I have always been interested in India, since my school days studying the close connection with India of our fellow countrymen, from setting up the East India Company and arrival of Clive in India. I had listened with fascination to many who served in the Indian Army.

It was therefore a great pleasure for my wife Pauline and I to fly to India on 8th December 2004 for virtually one month.

The Benedictine Ashram of Shantivanam in Tamil Nadu sent a vehicle to collect us from the airport of Tiruchirappalli, (or *Trichy),* to take us to Shantivanam Ashram close to the River Kaveri. The ashram had been founded by three French Benedictines.

In 1968 the English Benedictine Bede Griffiths arrived from England. Worship at the church, according to the Syrian Christian and Latin Benedictine traditions, was set out in the ashram prayer book, *Sandhya Vandana.* This was the meeting point of the church's liturgy of Christ and the rishis, of east and west, the creation of the said Bede Griffiths and his French predecessors.

We were met at the adjacent Ananda Ashram, preceded over by the indomitable and delightful Sr. Marie Louise. We were soon to suffer from the attentions of mosquitoes. Happily, there were mosquito nets over the beds in each chalet. I was ably assisted by a little team of friendly frogs and lizards. One frog used to wait outside the door to be let in the evenings: better than being eaten by the ever present paddy birds. Masilla, who looked after us, kindly disposed of a scorpion who ventured too close.

Pauline and I ventured along the banks of the River Kaveri and absorbed the sights and sounds of nature at its most beautiful. The sun was streaming through the trees. A bullock and cart were crossing the ford. Further down, boys were playing cricket on a sandbank.

My wife and I were persuaded to dress in an Indian outfit, of which we have a photo. One of the best aspects of this holiday were the many friendships we made with wonderful people from Germany, England, Canada, USA, Holland and Calcutta.

Along the banks of the Kaveri, people wash and carry out a cremation: death is accepted as a matter of course here. There is both a Hindu and a Christian graveyard on the river bank.

On 13th December we were honoured by the visit to Ananda Ashram of the best-selling author, Dominique Lapierre, writer of the *City of Joy* (i.e. Calcutta), and his wife. A number of us were invited to hear him talk after dinner about his experiences both of writing and of running charities in India. He donates half his royalties to the poor of Calcutta. Gaston Dayanand stayed in a nearby chalet: he looked after the poor and lepers of Calcutta, often working with Mother Theresa. We both felt very honoured meeting these two men.

December 17th was Bede Griffith's birthday. Bede's simple hut was left as it was the day he died, still pervaded by the spirit of this great Englishman. In addition, the entire village was invited to lunch and served by ashram workers. We found this a most moving experience. All of us were invited to a meal eaten from large banana leaves, sitting in a lotus position.

Not long after, we went to the opening of the kindergarten school and tailoring school. There was Indian dancing. I spent a happy hour distributing one sweet each to hundreds of joyful and well behaved children.

On 21st December we visited a spectacular temple in Srirangam. Then, on Christmas Day, we celebrated far from home. The church was decorated by flower garlands in memory of our son Philip on the seventh anniversary of his death.

The Tsunami tremors were felt at the ashram on the 26th December. We talked to a couple who had just returned from an awful car journey in which they were faced with a tsunami wave heading straight for them, preceded by fleeing people. They managed to rescue four people. Pauline arranged a hastily prepared candle lit vigil at the church and a collection for Tsunami victims. All in all, a very tragic day.

On 27th December, Pauline and I were driven to the airport at Tiruchippalli and we were flown back to Colombo, Sri Lanka. We were then flown back to the UK in another aircraft after a truly unforgettable month.

Not Your Average Solicitor's Office...

I was admitted as a Solicitor of the Supreme Court at the Law Society in 1982, after nineteen years as a Barrister in industry. I ran a Solicitor's branch office at Tilehurst, near Reading.

On 10th November 1986, I started work as a locum solicitor with Blackburn Gittings & Nott, a criminal law solicitor's firm in Westminster, to run their non-criminal work, so they could specialise completely in criminal law work.

I created a company with the name Ryan & Co. on 15th June 1987, on the top floor of Blackburn Gittings and Nott offices in Westminster. Blackburn Gittings & Nott passed me their non-criminal legal work from their clients who had criminal law problems. After some consideration, I accepted their top floor office to assist in setting me up in business on my own account as the firm of Ryan & Co., at their offices in Buckingham Palace Road.

A Transcendental Meditation colleague that I met at Roydon Hall, East Peckham, agreed to join the firm and did so on the 3rd August 1987. At the beginning she was just my Secretary, but it soon transpired that she was skilled enough to be my Personal Assistant and acted as the firm's internal Accountant and virtually as an Articled Clerk, and so it was. Initially, my clients were employees of the Queen at Buckingham Palace which was close by. Many of the rest were clients who had been accused of a crime, and came from Blackburn Gittings & Nott. Eventually, I used to joke that my clients were either defendants accused of crimes or aristocrats and this continued into my next office.

The business at the Buckingham Palace Road office expanded, so I had to expand the number of employees. On 23rd May 1988, I took much larger premises at Leader House, Shaftesbury Avenue, London, in the middle of Theatreland. The business became mainly buying and selling large hotels, and this became quite lucrative.

Ryan & Co. was an unusual, slightly idiosyncratic firm of solicitors, in that I only came to employ people practising Transcendental Meditation. All of my employees I met at or through the TM Academy at Roydon Hall, East Peckham, Kent. These included a part time actress from the London Repertory Theatre Company. All of us started and ended each day with a twenty minute meditation.

Interestingly, many clients remarked on the efficient, peaceful, and happy atmosphere in the office. We all knew precisely why this was and were delighted with these comments.

The business was also unusual in that the clients were split into two very distinctive elements, first, the aristocratic smart set and theatre clients and secondly the people accused of crimes that I had inherited from Blackburn Gittings & Nott. The former were mainly initially introduced to the firm by our meditating estate agent who had arranged to lease Leader House, where the office was, to my firm. We tried not to mix the two client groups in the office at the same time!

Another unusual aspect of the firm was that we all took it in turns to buy our vegetables etc. for lunch from the local market nearby, and the share in the preparation of the lunch in our kitchen. The others did not fare too well when I was the cook! In addition, I used to take all my employees on a tour of interesting places such as the nearby British Museum.

All in all, not quite your usual firm of solicitors. Happy days!

Regrettably, it all finished in June 1989 when I had to close the office because the economic climate had such a disastrous effect on the business of buying and selling hotels and property in general.

In addition to the commercial conveyancing, there was insufficient other business, like my probate business, to make it profitable in that venue. This was the time that many solicitors, particularly the small ones, closed.

With a heavy heart, I surrendered the lease and gradually ran the business down between my house in Wingham and that of my Personal Assistant, near Dartford for a year afterwards.

I survived financially by commencing locum work with nearby Mobil Oil Co. Ltd., 54 Victoria Street, SW1, on September 26th 1988. The Mobil Oil work was fascinating new work for me. After Mobil Oil, I commenced locum work from Croydon in the area of commercial conveyancing and town and country planning. The planning was most welcome because I needed this experience to use in future posts, which I did to great effect. In fact, latterly, planning became my new and strongest area of the law.

After Croydon, a local Deal Solicitor, wanted to lease the Old Stables attached to our house. The Old Stables Pauline and I had subsequently converted into an antique shop with her father's help. The solicitor planned to convert this into a solicitor's office as part of his business. I turned down this idea and he then offered me a post with his firm in Deal, Dover and Canterbury. I accepted his offer and worked in all three offices.

My Dementia Pathway

After my timely referral to a Senior Clinical Psychologist on the 19th January 2012, I underwent a long series of written tests at the Queen Victoria Memorial Hospital in Herne Bay and later at my home.

I was referred for an MRI scan on the 22nd April 2012. Having been diagnosed as having mixed dementia with Alzheimer's disease, I was then referred to the memory clinic at St Martin's Hospital in Canterbury.

After a hectic few days there was preoccupation and then a quiet acceptance of my own mortality, given my diagnosis. I cannot say enough for the Senior Clinical Psychologist and her competence and general helpfulness when visiting me at home. She kindly offered to keep me on her books for the time being, to which I readily agreed, even after completing my Cognitive Stimulation Therapy course. She visited me at home on 5th March, 2013.

On completion of this course, it became clear to me that I should join the Forget-Me-Nots Group in Canterbury. This proved to be an excellent decision.

The Group comprises of people living with dementia, clinical psychologists, university psychology placement students and a consultant clinical psychologist. Meeting by meeting I gradually learnt a considerable amount in order to play a more meaningful role in the Group.

I soon began a number of participatory activities such as

writing to Cabinet Ministers in response to questions posed to people with dementia, helping to interview and choose candidates for various posts at local memory clinics, and meeting and having a long and detailed conversation with the House of Lords.

Following my diagnosis of Mixed Dementia with Alzheimer's disease, I devised what I call my Daily Battle Plan!

With regards to tackling dementia, I very soon conceived the idea of creating a Battle Plan. As a result of which I really believe that I have slowed the down the progression of this condition.

The plan comprised of a number of different approaches and I shall happily summarize them to you one by one:

My Battle Plan

Acupressure for Memory and Understanding:
Acupressure is the ancient Chinese art of self-healing. I press the relevant acupressure points, thereby generating *a sense of harmony, health and wellbeing*. After using pressure on two particular points, I increased blood flow from virtually nil (considering I have two blocked arteries), to a very acceptable rate in just two weeks!

Applying pressure to another two points, pulses on both sides synchronised and I achieved a balance between both hemispheres of the brain.

I used the book, *Acupressure* by Michael Reed Gach (1992), to learn and understand more about acupressure.

Gym:

My wife and I attend the Kings School Recreation Centre, Canterbury, once every week. The first class I attended was a one-to-one exercise class, which was geared to each individual.

The Exercise Physiologist, who guided me through, kindly provided me with specially drawn up directions to carry out the exercises with appropriate diagrams of what to do and how to do it. I make sure this side of things is never neglected if time is short for whatever reason.

Reflexology Sessions:

I attend these sessions with a reflexologist from Holistic Health in Canterbury. At home I also use a reflexology massager. The body is divided up into ten longitudinal zones, five on each side of the vertical line. All the organs of the body are covered, including the brain.

I experienced an interesting problem. One toe in particular has a connection with the brain. I was getting pain regularly in that toe but only at night: nobody I asked knew about that one!

Transcendental Meditation (TM):

All in our family started to practice this several years ago. It reduces stress and increases efficiency, to all of which I can testify.

Transcendental Meditation aims to operate from the 'source of thought', a state of 'pure awareness,' to which I can also testify. Some years ago I operated from the source of thought for three weeks and found myself thinking at least twice as fast as I do usually, as a result of which many in my Company used to seek my opinion for a host of problems for that three weeks.

The Oxford Project to Investigate Memory and Ageing:

Quite early on, after my diagnosis, I wrote to the project director of the *Oxford Project to Investigate Memory and Ageing,* relating to vitamins B4, B6 and B12 and received his reply. This project has been working on a cure for Alzheimer's since before 2003. I like to stay up to date with research related to dementia as part of my daily battle plan.

Lasting Power of Attorney and Wills:

Being a retired Lawyer, one of my earliest actions was to prepare two draft Lasting Powers of Attorney, one for my wife and one for me. This was difficult as this was a new area of the law to me, so I decided to get a specialised firm of solicitors to check what I had done. The L.P.A was eventually sent to me by the Office of the Public Guardian.

Coconut Research Center, USA:

Much more recently, I contacted Dr. B. Fife of the Coconut Research Center in Colorado Springs, U.S.A. I wrote to him with regard to his important article at *www.coconutresearchcenter.org* on conquering Alzheimer's with Coconut Ketones. My email to Dr. Fife raised questions with regard to his new drug consisting of medium chain triglycerides (MCT's) that are converted into

Ketones in the body. This drug was approved by the US Federal Drug Administration for the treatment of Alzheimer's disease.

I had a helpful reply by return and I then went on to buy *Stop Alzheimer's Now.* I am now following his recommendations.

Choral Music Therapy:

I play CD's every day during my daily programmes at home, which induce an overall calm and happy serenity throughout. There some particular choices of music which I enjoy and I would like to tell you about a few of these.

a)   Rachmaninoff's Vespers

First comes, *Rachmaninoff's Vespers*, Tenebrae's *All Night Vigil* by Nigel Short and recorded live as part of the North Wales International Music Festival in St Asaph's Cathedral, St Asaph in 2004. The Russian singing has brought the really wonderful memories of many years ago, bringing back the Russian language I had learned from the White Russian Princess Coe (in York in what is now part of York University) when in the Intelligence Corps.

Great indeed was indeed the singing of *Priidite, Poklonimsya (Come, Let us worship)* and *Blagoslavi, Dushe Moya, Gospoda (Bless the Lord, O My Soul)*. I still have from the 1950s my old army exercise book full of Russian writing, and which came with us on Pauline and my cruise in 2005 to St. Petersburg.

b)   Kings College Chapel Choirs, Cambridge: The choral music & the peace on those heady days and after

The annual Christmas Eve (2012) TV broadcast covering the Festival of nine Lessons and Carols from King's College, Chapel, Cambridge, gently preceded us into Christmas. Christmas carols were the earliest form of vernacular choral literature.

Before the Reformation Catholic England combined English and Latin texts and then the Anglican Church gallantly built on this tradition. Now the wheel has turned full circle and the UK Ordinariate of Our Lady Walsingham has re-introduced her Festival of Nine Lessons and Carols initiated by King's College Chapel, much to the benefit of that Church. In addition, the Cambridge Singers' two CDs directed by John Rutter, *Lighten Our Darkness, Music for the Close of Day* was played, recorded in the Lady Chapel of Ely Cathedral in 2006.

c)   Mechtild of Magdeburg: *Songs of the Mystical Life*

Mechtild of Magdeburg (or Mechthild) (c.1210 - c.1282) a German 13th century Beguine mystic of the Cistercian nunnery of Helfta near Eisleben, known to us through her book *The Flowing Light of the Godhead,* written in her native Saxony. Her book is a kind of spiritual journal.

d)   John Rutter: Music for Christmas by the Cambridge Singers

A journalist has written: 'Rutter has become the musical equivalent of Dickens, synonymous with the season of Christmas'.

I appreciate Rutter's music as never before: it permeates and suffuses every fibre of one's being. It totally involves all one's senses. An intense love of music from some time in the past was reborn and reactivated with immense energy, this time with far more knowledge of the composers and their music.

Amazing to think it has taken eighty years for all this to flower in full bloom. What absolute joy!

e)   Margaret Rizza's Psalms

Some of Margaret Rizza's *Psalms* emanate from the *St. Thomas Music Group* directed by Rizza. They have appeared in her albums, *Fountain of Life, Fire of Love* and *Light on Our Darkness.* Rizza hauntingly beautiful melodies are 'recognised around the world as an icon in Christian Composition.'

f)   Clare College Choir, Cambridge: *Compline with Anthems and Motets*

Preceded by *Compline with Anthems and Motets*, I listen to the singing and music from Clare College, Cambridge. Composers included John Sheppard, William Byrd, Thomas Tallis, and Sergei Rachmaninov.

Clare Choir is considered one of the leading university choral groups in the UK. Clare I remembered well, having walked to work along a wonderful route twice a day for years across the Clare Bridge and through Clare, which I shall never forget.

g)   Tenebrae: Allegri Miserere

Signum Classics describe 'Allegri's haunting Miserere is the central point in a journey of longing and entreaty, hope and faith. These works spanning the centuries are chosen from the heart of Tenebrae's concert repertoire'. Two of the items were by the late John Tavener.

h)   John Tavener: BT Scottish Ensemble

I play the Orthodox Church's John Tavener's *Tears of the Angels, Depart in Peace* and *My Gaze is Ever Upon You*. Here was someone else who has experienced being preoccupied with his own mortality and whom Pauline and I had seen at a Canterbury Cathedral musical event recently.

i)   Spirit of Peace, Sounds from Ampleforth and hymns from St. Magnus Cathedral, Orkney

The Spirit of Peace CD, sung by the monks of Ampleforth Abbey, brings back memories of part of the traditional repertoire of sacred music known as *Gregorian Chant*. This wonderful CD commenced with *Vexilla Regis* and finished with the powerful *Christus Vincit*. I also played *Sounds from Ampleforth* and *Hymn to St Magnus*, performed by the St Magnus Cathedral choir, Kirkwall, Orkney.

j)   Buddhist Chants and Peace

Our CD *Buddhist Chants and Peace* music for reflection and relaxation from the Far East provides the beguiling temple sounds of Buddhism with an almost primal allure to the listener.

B. de Fréne

Writing in this section was supported by Lewis

The Day that Changed My Life

I opened my eyes. The room was dark except for the flickering light of the night-light on the chest of drawers. I saw my father with a pillow under his arm.

'What's the matter, Daddy?' I said.

'Hush,' he replied. 'You'll wake the others.'

'What are you doing?' I asked.

'There's a draught, blowing the night light. Now, go back to sleep!'

I saw my father put the pillow down behind the gas fire in the fireplace.

I woke again to find the room in complete darkness – the night-light must have gone out. I was aware that something soft and damp was in the bed – my nightdress was wet. I dimly realised that my baby sister was asleep next to me – how horrid! I thought, how did she get into my bed? Later on our nurse-maid lifted the baby out of the bed and told me to get up and take off my wet nightie. She then gave me my clothes to get dressed – it was very strange and still dark.

Down in the kitchen the range was burning warm and comforting. My grandmother and grandfather were there, sitting by the fire but still wearing their black overcoats. My grandmother was still wearing her large black hat.

'Drink your milk,' said my mother.

I hated milk.

'I don't like it,' I said.

'I'll put some sugar in it,' said my mother.

It was still horrible.

'You do make such a fuss,' said my mother. 'You need some food inside you. You are going with Gran to her house in Essex – it's a long drive!'

I felt sick. I always felt sick on long car journeys.

Barbara had eaten her porridge and drunk her milk.

'Why can't you be like Barb?' said my mother.

'Don't grumble at her!' said my Gran. 'She'll probably go to sleep in the car!'

It was still dark and cold when we got into the back seat of the car. The leather was slippery and cold and the thick blanket did not make me feel warm. The car started and went slowly down the drive.

I already felt sick.

We stayed with my grandparents for a year and returned to Ramsgate three months after war broke out. We were evacuated to Staffordshire two weeks later. My mother was living in a small bungalow. My father was not there.

I never saw my father again. His name was never mentioned in my hearing.

Waggie

My sister and I
Were four and five
When our 'Waggie'
Had six puppies.
Roly-poly 'sausages', soft and
Sweet, smelling of
Milk and fur.
We never knew why
One day
They went away.

A Gold Cross and Chain

I think that we never had much money, although we lived in a large house and kept several staff, including a cook and a nursery maid. My father kept hens in an orchard on the other side of the road and cultivated the large garden himself, with two enormous greenhouses with fruit like apricots and tomatoes in one, and in the other cucumbers and melons. His real 'job' was writing books, mainly on the history of dog breeds and research into spiders and insects.

The hairdresser, who was called Mr Blunt, came to the house to cut our hair once a month. One after another we were cloaked in the white cape, made to sit 'absolutely still' while the tickly hairs fell down the face and the horrid clippers went up the back of the neck. When the bob and fringe were finished, a soft brush went over our closed eyes, our noses, mouths and necks. I never enjoyed 'haircut days'!

One such day, just after my sixth birthday, Mr Blunt gave me a small blue leather-covered box. Inside was a gold cross and chain. I realised it was jewellery – something we had never had before. It was not pretty. It was not appropriate either: we were brought up agnostic. Religion was never mentioned. Worst of all, engraved on the back of the cross:

Billy, October 3rd 1938

Although I had never been to school, I knew my name was spelled 'Billie'.

On Being Evacuated to Staffordshire

I was six years old and my sister was five. We had returned from my grandparents' cottage in Essex and stayed for two weeks in a modern bungalow at Chiltern near Ramsgate. There was a funny pale green board, on a post, on the lawn in front of the house. My mother said it was to detect poison gas. I didn't understand, but it sounded very scary!

One morning the taxi arrived and we were taken, with our gas masks and very few belongings (Barbara carried her well-chewed 'Teddy Bear' but I had to leave mine behind as it was 'too large'). We arrived at the railway station in Ramsgate and joined a large group of children of a similar age, all with gas masks slung across their shoulders.

Many were crying. Many mothers were crying also. My mother was not, but could not bear to see the train depart. We were left with a teacher and made friends with some girls. My mother kissed us 'goodbye,' and left to take the taxi back to her bungalow.

The train journey was exciting, but very long. I was glad it was not a car journey, though I still felt sick. Barbara was crying, so I felt I couldn't cry. We got to Stafford. A woman tied a label on each of us, she said it was so that my sister and I wouldn't be separated.

Finally, a couple came forward and told us we were 'their evacuees'. The woman, unsmiling, took our hands. Her husband walked behind us and did not speak. Someone drove us to a village about fifteen miles from Stafford, out in the countryside, to a brand new council house that was so new that the garden was just rubble.

I did not cry; I felt that, although it was all horrible, the people were probably doing their best.

'Wren Pack,' Leaden Roding

My grandparents lived in a small cottage with a large, uncultivated garden and a ditch at the bottom, (or the 'brook' as my grandmother preferred to call it!), on which there were moorhens. There was no running water except for the pump over a stone sink in the kitchen. The 'privy' was right down the garden, near the ditch.

My grandmother had to light paraffin lamps in the evening and candles showed us the way to bed. Everything in the house had a funny smell – possibly from the oil or from the open fire or the stove in the kitchen.

Grandfather was often absent, still working at sixty-eight as a pilot on ships out of London. I didn't realise how dangerous this must have been until recently when I saw some documents from Trinity House.

Someone I Know

This piece of writing came in a session where Liz asked the writers questions, and we had to answer quickly, without any thinking time, just writing the first response that came into our minds.

- *Write the name of someone you know*

My sister, Barbara Jean Anne. She's eleven months younger than I am. Her pet name was 'Deeo'.

- *List anything that comes into your head as you think of that person*

Four years old

Driveway

Doll's Pram

McIntosh cape

Raining

No clothes underneath

Driveway to road

Bus stop

Lady with a shopping basket

'Are you two twins?'

'No, we're gentleman's daughters.'

Gates

Not allowed to go out.

- *Tell me what's inside that person's refrigerator?*

It's fairly empty: meat - not wrapped, not covered (she argues with me about bacteria). Very little else – some butter, goats cheese. It's a very large refrigerator, as she lived in Spain.

- *What would she do with £100?*

Buy a bottle of brandy – and several more maybe!

- *Think about food you have shared with this person - what comes to mind?*

I have a photograph of my sister and me fighting over a glass of something, juice or cordial. My sister's eleven months younger than I, by the time she was four she was taller than I was.

- *What smells are you reminded of when you think of her?*

I think she smoked at the time, when I last saw her in Greece; since I didn't smoke I was always conscious of other people smelling of cigarettes.

- *When you picture this person, where are they?*

At home, on her boat; it's very tidy, and very sparsely furnished.

- *What made you choose this person?*

She's my younger sister; it just came into my head how I miss her.

- *What is she doing when you think of her now?*

She doesn't communicate now - I don't know why - it's all mixed up with things that have happened since the last time I saw her on her boat in 1956.

- *If you could ask her a question right now, what would it be?*
Couldn't you just keep in touch?

A Stoneware Pot

I have a tall stoneware vase. It is a good shape with imaginative glazing – a fine piece of 'Canterbury Pottery'. The vase was a present I was given when I was leaving the school where I had been teaching for almost seven years.

Mark was a third year boy who came to my after-school cookery club. He was bigger than most of the other boys of his age and very assertive – sometimes quite a pain in the neck! I often had to reprimand him for his boisterous behaviour – not appropriate in a Home Economics room! I sometimes felt that I grumbled at him too much – after all, it was a voluntary club.

On the last day of term, Mark came to my room and handed me a large, carefully wrapped parcel. He said, 'I bought this for you, Miss, to thank you for teaching me to cook.'

I unwrapped the beautiful vase and was so overcome that I wept.

Chris N

Thanks to my gorgeous wife, Rachael, who is my harbour of peace and serenity in the sometimes stormy and tumultuous seas of life.

Writing in this section was supported by Sophie

Memories of Rosemary Cottage

Rosemary Cottage is situated in the village where I grew up, which nestles beside the River Thames in Royal Berkshire. In 1602, two cottages were built for staff at the Manor House and some 150 years ago, these two cottages were joined together to form Rosemary Cottage.

It's a Grade Two listed building, consisting of numerous oak beamed rooms and odd shaped hidey-holes. It is possible to sit within the alcove where the fireplace is, but best not when it's lit!

Above the front door is a metal plaque for the Sun Alliance, dating back to the days when fire brigades, run by insurance companies, would only answer a fire-call if you were a member. If not, the house was allowed to burn down!

Over its 400 years, it has been a butcher's, a 19th Century coffee shop, a laundry, Civil Defence offices during World War II, as well as being a residential property.

In my early years, I had friends that lived in the house and many happy games of hide-and-seek were played there in all the nooks and crannies. In 1969, while I was away at scout camp, my family moved into Rosemary Cottage. They did, however, let me know where they had moved to!

Rosemary Cottage adequately accommodated my parents and we six children. It took some getting used to the low beams, and the fact that it never stopped creaking and making strange sounds, particularly at night. There is not a single right-angled wall, ceiling, door or window in the whole of Rosemary Cottage and pieces were cut off the tops of doors and added to the bottom to make them fit.

It had a mischievous poltergeist, which would make things disappear and re-appear in the most obvious of places, and the family dogs would regularly be seen staring into the corners of rooms, their hackles up and low-growling.

On one occasion, an army friend came round and would not believe my stories about the poltergeist. While we were talking, half of his pint of beer had disappeared from his glass when we looked back at it. This said, we were never put in fear by our extra resident.

Memories of Army Days (Boy Service)

It has to be said that when we look back on life, we often do so through rose tinted spectacles and we find humour in what, at the time, was possibly difficult to deal with.

I joined the Army in 1969 as a musician in HM Life Guards Band, part of the Household Cavalry, and served until 1975. I was fifteen years old when I went to The Guards Depot in Pirbright, Surrey.

I was in a man's world but it has to be understood that, at this time, I was five foot tall, blond haired, blue-eyed, had a well-spoken soprano voice and a slight lisp. Life was going to be a challenge and I ensured that I slept with my back to the wall every night!

My accommodation was on the third floor of the Junior Musicians Wing. Unfortunately, all the issued clothes were designed for soldiers of six foot in height, so I rattled around inside my green denims, which hung off me loosely.

One night, I was larking about with the trained soldier in charge of our wing, and I threatened to throw his towel out of the window. He said that if I did so, then I would follow. Not believing that he meant it, I threw the towel out. Next thing I knew, I was hanging upside down outside the window, third floor up from the ground, and I was rapidly slipping out of my ill-fitting denims. It was only my large boots that stopped me completely sliding out of the trained soldier's grip as he tried to haul me back inside.

It was not long after this, we were practicing marching in band formation. Somehow, I had got out of step with the others and I was out of alignment with the rest of my rank. The Drum Major then proceeded to advise me of my errors in no uncertain terms. When he had finished, he asked me if I understood the error of my ways.

Now, for the life of me, I don't know why I did it, but I gave him my best smile.

I told him I had taken on board what he had yelled at me and gave him a cheeky wink!

All hell broke loose!

He apparently took exception to being winked at by a soldier in his ranks and exploded with a string of expletives that cannot be printed here. Needless to say, he was not impressed! It has to be said that in the early days of my training, I was just not quite getting the hang of this army lark!

Every Saturday morning, the whole of the Junior Guards Depot assembled on the Drill Square to practice marching. One particularly bitter winter's morning, I had been delayed, cleaning my kit for the parade, and had not had time to go to breakfast. Before going on parade, you should always ensure you have food inside you or you are likely to faint. This is particularly important if it is hot or very cold weather.

Realising this and having no time to get a breakfast, I reasoned that if I scoffed half a box of Jaffa Cakes, this would probably suffice: wrong!

We got on parade, but the weather was so extremely cold, even the valves on our instruments froze. Gradually, this horrible feeling of dizziness and nausea came over me.

Now it has to be understood that the Drill Square is hallowed ground in the army and must be treated with due respect and reverence. It is always kept immaculately clean.

Well, the combination of the cold and the Jaffa Cakes took its toll on me and I proceeded to be sick onto the Drill Square. This was not a wise thing to do.

Long after the parade had finished, I could be seen on my hands and knees with a bucket and scrubbing brush. The clear instructions I had been given by the Regimental Sergeant Major were that, when he returned to inspect the offending area, it should be good and clean enough for him to eat his dinner off.

At least I didn't have to do it with my toothbrush! Another valuable life lesson was learnt that the army marches on its stomach but not on its contents on the ground!

The following summer, we gave a concert to entertain the Guards Depot and one of the pieces consisted of Sea Shanties. Yes, you've guessed it. Imagine my humiliation as there I was, dressed up on stage as a Cabin Boy, trilling my Soprano heart out in front of hundreds of tough guy soldiers.

For weeks afterwards, everywhere I went, there were wolf whistles. Thankfully, soon after this, my voice broke and I grew ten inches over the space of a year.

Time moved on and, having attained the ripe old age of seventeen, I moved onto Regular Man Service. I left the Junior Guards Depot behind to start the next chapter in my dubious service to Queen and Country.

Memories of Army Days (Man Service)

In September 1969, I enlisted in the Army and became a part of HM Life Guards Mounted Band. Having served for two years on Boy Service at the Guards Depot in Pirbright, Surrey, I moved onto Man Service and began a new chapter in my life.

From 1971 to 1972, I was at Kneller Hall School of Army Music. During the springtime of 1972, we were all assembled in the Concert Hall for a practice. Above us, outside on the flat roof, there were workmen busy carrying out re-tarring and maintenance work.

When the band was not playing, there were some odd creaks and groans to be heard coming from the roof. Suddenly, with a loud bang, the ceiling collapsed and a workman, with his tar-machine, came tumbling down from above. I faced a quick decision. Should I run towards the walls - which were coming inwards - or should I shelter under my chair?

I chose to run towards the walls and watched as a beam descended from the ceiling and crushed my vacated chair flat.

We all struggled out of the hall for a roll call to find that there had only been a few minor injuries among us, which included the workman who had come through the roof. We definitely brought the house down that day!

Up to the middle of the 1970s, I was part of the State Trumpet Fanfare Team, and we carried out engagements both on foot and mounted on our horses across Great Britain and on the Continent. Our uniform consisted of a metal ornate helmet with a long horse-haired plume hanging from the top, red tunic with a white cross belt and waist belt, tight black trousers and spurred boots.

On one occasion, we had carried out a Fanfare at the very posh Café Royal Hotel in London from a closed-in balcony above the audience. Having finished, we went off to change. A message was then sent to us that another fanfare was required promptly, so we charged back onto the balcony and blew another fanfare. What the big-wigs below did not know was that all of us were trouser-less behind the balcony but looking very grand from the waist up.

At the Colchester Tattoo, this time we were all mounted on our horses for the final dress rehearsal and all the participants in the Tattoo were assembled in the arena. We blew our opening fanfare. What we did not know was that there was a fly-over by three Harrier Jets as we finished. Needless to say, the jets flying over startled the horses which shot off in all directions, trampling over the assembled masses in the Arena and leaving the area looking like Custer's Last Stand.

Occasionally, we carried out corporate events. At one in Inverness for a well-known boiler manufacturer, Henry Cooper came into the room carrying a boiler on his shoulders, the slogan being 'Heavy Weight Champion of the World'.

There we were in all our finery, with our white horse-hair plumes hanging down. We blew the fanfare as he made his way to the stage. For his opening remark of his speech, he turned towards us and said 'In years gone by, I was surrounded by blond haired beauties, but look what I have been reduced to now!'

When people start to talk about Football, I like to casually drop into the conversation that I have played at Wembley. People that know me are in no doubt that it wasn't as a footballer!

I was taking part in the Wembley Pageant in the Wembley Stadium, and was again mounted on my horse, blowing a fanfare. The Fanfare Team regularly played tricks on each other, and this day turned out to be no exception.

The Fanfare Trumpet had a gold-thread inlaid banner and, hanging down on each leading edge, there were coloured cords with tassels on the end. We raised our trumpets for the fanfare. As it started, no matter how hard I blew, hardly any sound was coming out.

What I hadn't realised was that the trumpeter next to me had shoved one of the tassels up the bell-end of my trumpet. I blew harder and suddenly the tassel flew out of the end of my trumpet, which then emitted a loud blare of sound that any elephant would have been justly proud of. Luckily, as there were eight trumpeters, it was impossible for the audience to tell who the noisy offender was but I quietly plotted my revenge for another day…

There was one occasion, however, when blowing a fanfare did me an unexpected favour.

Back in the Seventies at the cinema, the main feature was always accompanied by a Pathé News feature.

I had taken my very-new girlfriend to watch the film 'Jaws'. I thought it would make her jump in places and this would be a perfect opportunity for me to put a protective arm around her. (You have to watch young lads, they can be very devious!)

As we watched the Pathé News, suddenly up onto the silver screen came a close-up of me, on my horse, at the Royal Windsor Horse Show blowing a fanfare for the Queen's arrival.

Now, this was a result on two fronts. Firstly, my new girlfriend jumped to her feet and yelled out 'That's my boyfriend,' clearly establishing how she felt about me and, secondly, I could now add starring on the silver screen to my repertoire of chat-up lines!

As I have said before, sometimes we carried out corporate events. One such occasion was at the Dorchester Hotel in London. This was for a Jewish bar mitzvah. Bizarrely, there was a young lioness in a cage in the foyer of the hotel as part of the ceremony.

After everyone had arrived, we had played the fanfare and the event was underway, I returned to the foyer for another look at the lioness. I was still dressed in my red tunic. As the lioness was no longer needed, the owners were moving her from the show cage into the tunnel leading to their travel vehicle.

Just how it happened, I don't know, but suddenly the lioness had escaped and was wandering around the foyer. I hid behind an ornate pillar, mindful of the fact that in my red tunic, I probably looked like a very tasty piece of juicy meat to the lioness. Thankfully, the handler grabbed the lioness and she went off down the tunnel to her travel vehicle while the colour gradually returned to my cheeks. They say 'curiosity killed the cat,' but my fear was that the proverb would be reversed!

On another occasion, we were at Brands Hatch. The winner of the race stood on the rostrum in front of us. We blew the fanfare for the presentation and remained static while he opened the champagne. In the finest racing tradition, he sprayed the champagne. He then turned towards us and squirted the champagne all over us, soaking our uniforms. Needless to say, I knew what I wanted to do with my trumpet, banner, bell-end and all!

Just some of the memories from many years ago that are still so clear and vivid in my mind, as if it was yesterday. It is so frustrating that the things that have happened to me in more recent times have become so blurred and hard to recall.

However, I will continue to stubbornly fight the good fight with dementia. It isn't about to win yet!

A Village Policeman's Lot

I'll never forget the time when I was a Village Policeman near Sevenoaks in 1980.

I was living in the Police House and my son was about six months old. My sister came to stay over a weekend with her nine month old baby daughter, her husband and their dog.

All was peace and quiet, until 3am on the Sunday morning, when the doorbell went. There then followed a chain reaction. The doorbell sounding caused both my dog and my sister's dog to start barking furiously.

This woke the two babies who, at the top of their lungs, like banshees from hell, both started to scream the house down. Dutifully, the young mothers rose from their beds to attend to and pacify their upset offspring. Now, new fathers are famously pretty good at sleeping through their newborn's cries in the middle of the night but, with the added backing-group chorus provided by the dogs, this was not to be the case. The whole household was now awake.

Having quickly thrown some clothes on, I dashed to the front door to attend to what must be a Very Important Emergency to wake us all in the middle of the night.

There stood a young mother on my doorstep, with a babe in arms swaddled tightly against the cold night air. Whatever it is that has happened, it must be very serious for them both to be out on a night like this, I mused. I asked the young woman what had occurred, adrenaline mounting and ready to spring into action.

She then proceeded to tell me the shocking story in all its gory detail.

There was a fox at the end of her garden that was howling, keeping her baby awake. What did I suggest she should do?

Moments passed with complete silence from me while I struggled to phrase a suitable, polite response, far from what I really thought she should go and do!

Memories of being a Driving Instructor

Back in the early 1990s, I trained as a driving instructor. To say the least, life was rarely boring and I never knew just what challenge was round each corner from day to day.

One particular lady that I taught, even now, brings a smile to my face when I recall her eccentricity, and the journey that we had together to enable her to successfully obtain a Full Driving Licence.

She had taken some lessons before meeting me, but said she was changing her instructor because the previous one didn't seem to have a sense of humour. This should have warned me as to what was to come!

Now, as was normal practice, on the roof of my car I had a name board with L-plates on, which was placed behind the Sunroof, so that it could be clearly visible. She settled herself into the car and adjusted the rear view mirror. She then burst into laughter and exclaimed that she could see I had a sense of humour, and that what I had done was a very funny trick to play.

I was puzzled and asked her what she meant. She replied that I had put the name board across the back window so she couldn't see out. I then realised what she had done. When she adjusted the rear view mirror, she had tilted it so high that it was giving a view up through the sunroof towards the sky, with the roof-board blocking her view!

A few weeks later, on another lesson, we were approaching a crossroads, where we were going to turn right. The mirrors were checked correctly, the right indicator was applied and the correct position was taken up in the road, ready to turn right. All was going fine, text book stuff.

She looked into the junction to the right: all was clear to turn, and I naturally assumed we would turn right.

Without any warning, she suddenly steered to the left, and attempted to turn into the road, on the left! I whipped my head round, at a speed likely to cause whip-lash, to check that there were no vehicles passing on our inside, but thankfully, there was nothing there! We pulled over and I explained the error of her ways while my heartbeat calmed back to a normal rate! It just goes to show that if you assume anything, it could make an ASS of U and ME.

As the course of the lessons progressed over the weeks, various bizarre things occurred, just a couple of which I'll outline here.

We had reached the point for me to teach the 'Reverse Around a Left Corner'. We had stopped, and were getting ready to carry out the manoeuvre. I advised her that she needed to get into a position where she could have a good view out of the back window. There was a click of her seatbelt being released and, next thing I knew, she was kneeling on her seat, looking out of the back window. Through a stifled laugh, I asked her how she was going to reach the pedals and also steer. It was all too much when she replied that she would have to stretch a bit, and we both descended into fits of uncontrolled laughter, with tears rolling down our cheeks!

On another occasion, we were going to carry out the 'Turn in the Road' exercise, commonly known as the three-point-turn. The idea is to turn the car around to face the opposite direction, by using the full width of the road. We had carried out the first part and driven forward across the road. We were now doing the second part, with us reversing across the width of the road. As we did so, she said she could no longer see the kerb behind us and I advised her that she could look out of the driver's side window to enable her to see the kerb.

There then followed a loud thump and she started to rub her forehead and I could see a grease mark on the driver's window. I advised her that it was probably best to open the window first!

The day before the Driving Test had arrived. She said that she was nervous, which was understandable, but would it be alright if she wore her lucky troll? I said it would, knowing that it would help her feel less on edge.

The following morning, I picked her up for her test. She came out of her house and got into the car: she had six small, multi-coloured-hair trolls, pinned down the front of her jumper like military buttons. Around her neck, on a leather boot-lace, she had a troll about six inches tall with bright purple Day-Glo hair.

I asked her, through gritted teeth to stop me laughing, whether she really needed all the trolls, but she insisted she needed all the luck that they would bring. I was inclined to agree with her!

We arrived at the Test Centre and took our seats in the Waiting Room. I shall never forget the look on the female Driving

Examiner's face when she entered the room, called out my pupils name and beheld this bizarre apparition in front of her.

I tried, with all my self-control, to not laugh out loud when I saw the Examiner's face turn from initial shock, through a smile and then the Examiner left the room, with her shoulders starting to shake as she descended into laughter. The Examiner came back into the room a moment or two later, with watery eyes from laughing and, having got herself back under control, proceeded off on test with my pupil.

When they got back, the lady had passed her test and the Examiner walked passed me with the parting comment that seeing my pupil dressed up like that had been the best thing that had happened to her in years.

Bella: The Black Beauty

We had always wanted a German Shepherd dog. When the children were small, we tried out a Rescue Alsatian that had been mistreated, but it kept nipping them all the time and we felt it could not be trusted. Sadly, we had to give it back.

Some twelve years ago, we purchased a twelve week old German/Belgium Shepherd cross puppy. Her mother was black haired and the father was white haired. As she grew, she had the black coat of her mother, a white under carriage of her father and, bizarrely, brown tanned legs.

She was never going to win a prize at Crufts but she was beautiful to us.

Dogs take on the nature and demeanour of the household they live in and Bella was no exception. She was just a big old softy and loved to spend her time lying down with her legs in the air, her tummy all exposed. However, if somebody knocked the door, she assumed the role of family protector, barking and growling in a deep voice, pretending for all the world that she was going to eat the caller whole!

She had endless energy for a game of chase the ball or stick, and her big brown eyes looked so disappointed when her stamina-depleted thrower decided to stop!

She was always pleased to see us, even if we had only been out of the house for five minutes. She would come bounding up, her eyes all bright and her bushy tail wagging so hard, that she nearly turned herself inside out with excitement.

She was always inquisitive as to what we were doing and would follow us from room to room to ensure that she didn't miss out on what was going on. She regarded the lawn mower as a threat and would be close beside me when I went to the shed to get it out. When the electric motor was started, she would bark at the mower and bite its wheels initially, in a protective manner, to show it who was boss.

She was accepting when my daughter's cat became a permanent resident in the household and would cuddle up lovingly with it but yet when it was in the garden, she would chase after it playfully, barking madly, with no real intention of catching it. When my daughter-in-law's young Guide Dog was introduced into the household, she welcomed her in but definitely kept the young whipper-snapper in her place, on occasions, to show her who was the Boss.

In October last year, she passed away and we lost a loving, loyal member of our family - but her memory lives eternally within our hearts and souls.

The Love and The Gold Ring

My wedding ring is made of bright gold, and is one of a pair that my wife and I wear.

It was perfectly round thirty-six years ago, but has now moulded to the shape of my finger. On the outer surface, there was a 'tree-bark' effect. This has now been virtually smoothed away with the years of constantly being on my finger. However, the love that it signifies has not similarly diminished or worn away with time.

The love and the gold ring; over the years, have both withstood the rough and tumble that life can inflict, to emerge still shining out like a beacon in the night.

Like the gold ring, my wife and I have moulded and adapted so that we still remain a perfect fit for each other.

Like the gold ring, our love continues endlessly and is there for all to see.

Although of no great financial value, in terms of emotional value, it is priceless.

Life is a Journey - not a Destination

The last five years have certainly caused me to view my life in a very different way and learn to live for, and in, the moment. Life will always throw challenges at us but, as long as we get up and fight one more time, we are not beaten.

Let me explain.

At the age of eleven, I started to learn to play the trumpet and subsequently joined the army as a musician in HM Lifeguards' Band. On leaving the army, I became a police officer in Kent Police, and was a founder member of the Kent Police Band. I was able to continue my playing, but now played Tenor Horn.

In 2008, I had two heart attacks which hospitalised me, and a further heart attack in 2009. I am now fitted with seven stents. I was told by my doctors to stop playing as this appeared to be putting an undue strain on my heart. I followed the advice but I desperately missed playing, something I had done for over forty-four years.

As I recovered from the third heart attack, I contracted Shingles, as my immune system was low. This manifested itself mainly on my face and forehead. Luckily, although my eyes were infected, no permanent damage was caused to my sight.

Over the next couple of years, a level of tiredness and exhaustion set in like I had never known before. I was eventually diagnosed with M.E. (Chronic Fatigue Syndrome) which was a result of the Shingles virus.

I had reached a crossroads in my life. I could give in, submit and deteriorate or I could fight back. I decided firmly in my mind to rise to, and overcome this challenge. The battle was not done yet, and I would emerge the victor!

During 2012, it became increasingly apparent to my family, my work colleagues and to me that a change was occurring.

I was starting to mix up my words, I was getting confused with regard to things that had happened in the recent past, and I appeared to be just becoming vague when in conversation.

At the time, I was employed as a Driving Examiner. The nature of my work during the driving test of candidates required me to remember what, when and where things had happened in order to debrief the test and then accurately write up the report afterwards. I noticed that this was becoming increasingly hard for me to do, and needed far greater and more intense concentration to do so.

I made the first of a series of visits to my doctor's practice. I was given the standard dementia test which I appeared to have no problem with.

Dementia was ruled out as being the problem.

It was suggested that I might be suffering from depression. Having been clinically depressed and having had a nervous breakdown in 1990, I knew how I was feeling had nothing to do with depression.

Over that year, I made a series of visits to the G.P. My symptoms were getting slowly worse with no remedy being found. I visited another G.P. within the practice. He again carried out the standard dementia test, which again did not flag up dementia problems. The G.P. said that certain types of dementia did not show up using the standard test and, this time a referral was made for me to the Memory Clinic.

It had now become impossible for me to continue working, and although I made two attempts to go back to work, both times I only managed a couple of days before my manager, seeing that I was not coping, suggested that I return to 'sick' status.

I subsequently attended the Memory Clinic where a series of in depth tests were carried out. In December, 2012, as a result of these tests, I was diagnosed with 'fronto-temporal dementia'.

It was clear that there was a problem with regard to my executive functioning. This was the ability to put things correctly, sequentially, when given in a random order. I also had various scans but these did not show up any significant abnormalities. I was assured that this was not unusual as, in ten to fifteen per cent of cases of fronto-temporal dementia, it did not show up on the scans.

As a result of the diagnosis and there being no cure, I was forced to retire from work.

Although it is never good to get a diagnosis of dementia, it was a great relief to finally establish the cause of the challenges that I was having in everyday functioning. I was now able to explain to family and friends the reasons why my demeanour and behaviour was sometimes different from the person they all knew well.

The overall effect that my fronto-temporal dementia has on me can be summed up in the famous Morecombe and Wise sketch with André Previn, where Eric Morecombe said 'I'm playing all the right notes but not necessarily in the right order!'

I have now done two courses of Cognitive Stimulation Therapy. The first was in a group (We called ourselves the 'Happy Wanderers' which was quite apt) and the second course was on a one-to-one basis and I have had Speech Therapy. These treatments have allowed me to expand on the coping strategies that I have put in place to help me cope with my daily challenges.

On conclusion of the Cognitive Stimulation Therapy, I joined the Forget-Me-Nots group. I have found being part of this group to be very stimulating - it is good to exchange thoughts and views with my peers on numerous subjects surrounding dementia and coping mechanisms.

Since joining the group, I have been involved in six projects and there are a number in the near future. Recently, the Forget-Me-Nots have been involved in a Life Writing project which is how this book came about. Members of the group have been featured on the radio talking about the book and their very diverse experiences of life's twists and turns.

The group certainly gets us out and about! There are about twenty of us in The Forget-Me-Nots and we are greatly supported and aided by psychology students.

I find this group very stimulating and the feeling of friendship and community goes a long way to reassure all our group members that they are not alone in the strange, and sometimes confusing, world of dementia.

It is now very difficult for me to put things in a correct

sequence, even down to the order of the letters in the alphabet, which is something learnt at an early age.

As a result of my diagnosis, I decided to live life to the full and went back to playing my Tenor Horn. Most weekends I can be found on a bandstand somewhere in Kent, or further afield. It has become increasingly difficult to read the music correctly and, like words, it is now harder to get the information off the page in the correct order and sequence. This applies to all aspects of my thinking process where a correct sequence of events is required.

It is my belief that, when life throws challenges at us, we should face them head-on and fight back. I have adopted the daily mantra of 'I may have dementia but dementia does not have me!' In the famous words of Winston Churchill: 'Never, never, never, give up!'

Chris R

For the many happy and loving years together,

and hopefully many more,

to my wife, Andrea Ryan

Writing in this section was supported by Lewis

Swimming Badges

I was apprehensive when joining the life writing group. I didn't think it would be my thing – how wrong could I be?

On the first day Liz, our teacher, gave out some words for us to think about. It's amazing, what comes into your head. One of the words she said was 'Swimming Badges'. I thought, 'Swimming badges'? What could I write about those? Then, from nowhere, came:

10 yards

20 yards

100 yards

Different colour badges

Jumped in, swam as quick as I could and came second.

This was something that happened to me over fifty years ago. These words sparked memories in my head. From then on, I was hooked. I have loved it, and would recommend it to anyone with or without dementia. It was very stimulating.

Me and my dementia

My dementia... Where do I start? About four years ago in 2010, my wife said she started to notice I was doing strange things, little things, like starting one thing and going onto something else before finishing the last job, forgetting where I put stuff – silly things at the time that were put down to getting older, and that old saying, 'Oh, we all do that'. What an annoying saying that turned out to be!

After she kept saying that she would be worried if it were her, I went to the doctors, but my problems were blamed on my medication for my other ailments, like diabetes, hypertension, osteoarthritis and depression. So, home I went to explain what the doctor said, and to say don't worry, I'm okay.

About four months later I'm back there again. Same answer, I'm okay.

Three months later I took my wife with me and she told the doctor about what I had been doing and saying, and, *bingo!* I get a referral to the assessment, which threw up a few problems, so I was referred to a consultant psychologist for more tests.

I had a CT scan, an MRI scan, both of which didn't show anything abnormal, but my consultant was sure I had something wrong, and I was sent for a SPECT scan. This showed an abnormality, and from there, after more tests, I was given a diagnosis of fronto-temporal dementia.

What a relief this was for me and my wife! Now we had a name for what was wrong with me, and we could now move on with our lives.

We thought we would just jog along as normal, but as we know, that's not what happens.

I have gotten worse, and it has become much harder for my wife. Our roles are reversing. I used to do everything: banking, bills, paperwork, and the day-to-day organising of things. It's like I have stepped back and she has stepped forward.

Also, now I don't like noise, confrontation, crowds – I just want a quiet life.

Another problem is that I say what I see, and it doesn't matter where we are, I will just say it, whereas before I might think it and say nothing. Now, I just say it, and that can be very embarrassing for my wife. Not me, because I don't realise that I've said anything wrong.

We tell everyone what I have and find that helpful. The only problem with this is, (here's that saying again), 'Oh I do that', 'We all do that.' No, you don't, unless you have a diagnosis of dementia.

Yes, everybody does forget things as you get older, but with dementia it is so much more than that, not just forgetting a few things or putting the milk in the microwave by mistake. As my wife says, have a day in her life and then you'll see what really goes on.

We have been very lucky with the support we have received from the carers' service, the mental health team, the Dover Lifeboat old boys, and the group, the Forget-Me-Nots. This group has been a great support to me. It's run by people with different dementias. We have two consultant psychologists, and some psychology students, on hand to help with the paperwork and organising different meetings and events for us to attend, but the meetings are run by us.

I would not have been writing this book if it were not for them, and I wouldn't have spoken at dementia conferences. Were it not for them, I wouldn't have sat on interview panels. If it were not for them, I would not have spoken at memory clinics for newly diagnosed people with dementia, telling them what they can do, and what help is available for them, like driving tests, clubs to join, Carers' Society for their partners and so on.

There is a lot out there for us, and we're getting more and more as people become more aware of dementia. This group has given me a purpose.

There is life after diagnosis; you just have to adjust to what you can do. Your whole lifestyle changes. You are lucky if you have good family and friends around you.

Every day is different, but it's like that in real life, so try to enjoy it.

Albany Place, Dover

I moved to Albany Place in 1978, when I was twenty three years old. The house was over 150 years old. It had one bedroom but was very spacious. It had a spiral staircase in the middle of the lounge made from a tree trunk, with pine steps, and rope handrails.

Our house in those days, you could leave your door open all day without worrying about someone coming in. The whole street was like this, all looking out for one another.

There was an old graveyard at the back of the house going up to the historic moats. We used to play with the kids in the street, sliding down on bits of cardboard and tin down the hills. If any animal died, they used to come to me. I think I was the animal undertaker!

On bonfire night we used to have a great big fire for the kids (and us). There were lots of fireworks, hotdogs, burgers, sandwiches, sweets and a lot of drink. What great times, and great memories.

Sadly, those times are gone forever.

I'll Never Forget the Time…

I'll never forget the time I was called out on the lifeboat. It was at about 05:20 on the morning of the 16th October, 1987. Our bleepers didn't go off, but luckily I heard the maroons go off. At that time the wind was blowing at about seventy miles per hour, and gusting at a hundred.

I can always remember, as I was pulling away in my car, our neighbour Debbie came out and said to my wife, 'You're not letting him go, are you?'

She said 'I can't stop him, it's what he does.'

Then, looking up, there was a six by six foot fence panel floating above the house opposite.

'That's strange', I thought, still half asleep, and went on my way to the lifeboat.

All the way there I was getting battered by flying debris. When I got to the boat, I was the last of our seven crew to get there. I was still thinking it wasn't too bad, just blowing a bit. But once I got aboard, I went into the cabin, and Geoff, a school teacher and our radio operator, had all his life saving gear on.

I said, 'Why have you got all that on?'

He said 'That's bloody rough out there!'

That's the first time I had ever seen Geoff with all his gear on. He was right, it was rough. We had been called out to the ferry Hengist, but she had run aground off of Folkestone and seemed to be okay. It was the other one that was our job now.

Our coxswain, Roy, a garage owner and lifeboat second

coxswain mechanic, said 'The other one.'

'Yes a small ship called the Sumnia,' the coastguard said. She was getting blown towards Dover by the weather, she had her anchors out but nothing would hold her in those seas. We let go and tried to leave the berth, but there was a rope around our propeller, stopping us dead.

From somewhere we had two divers go into the water to try to free the rope. They did what they could but we had to go, as the ship was nearly at the harbour entrance. We set off again, and this time we managed to get off the berth. The wind was now 100mph constant.

We could not see a thing going past the Prince of Wales pier, just metres away, nothing. There was lots of stuff in the water, a fuel bowser that had been blown off the quay, went floating off with lots of other debris. Then, out of the spray and spume we saw her.

She was getting battered against the breakwater, rising as high as the lighthouse. We realised that there were two men on the bow, so we tried to get in as close as possible so we could get them off. Eric, a Royal National Lifeboat Institution employee, and myself, went up to our bow and shouted to them, 'JUMP!'... But would *you* in those seas?

Luckily for them and us, a huge wave came over and washed them off into the boiling sea. Dom, a publican, and Eric, managed to get them out of the sea and onto the lifeboat. Then Robert, a policeman, and myself, got them into the cabin with Geoff. They didn't seem to have any injuries at that time.

Then, we swung around the outside of the Sumnia, looking for more survivors. It was too rough to get close to her as she was gradually breaking up. I remember looking back and seeing blue and white flashes as she finally broke in half and sank.

We turned to sea to get a better position to navigate down the back of the breakwater, but we encountered a massive wave which we managed to climb, but fell off the top of.

It was about seventy feet high. Our coxswain was badly injured by this and the lifeboat nearly capsized, but she managed to right herself just in time before the next big one came. The rest of us were quite wet from being underwater for most of the time.

Then a call came from port control, saying that they thought they could see a lifejacket floating in the eastern entrance of the harbour. We steamed down the outside of the harbour to the entrance.

I shouted up to Mick, a train driver who was on the flying bridge with Roy; there was something in the water on our starboard side. I thought it was one of the missing crew, but he said that it was a lump of wood.

To this day I still wonder if it was the missing captain.

This is where we nearly went over again, but the coxswain did us proud and got us to where the lifejacket was. At first we thought it was just a jacket, but on pulling it up there was a man underneath. We got him aboard but he was lifeless.

Roy shouted down, 'Get working on him!' We got him down to the aft cabin where two of us worked on him. In the end Robert kicked him in the stomach, and he started breathing again.

By now we were heading back to the berth to get the casualties off. After this we went back out, as there were still two men missing.

After about twenty minutes, our coxswain was feeling bad so we had to get him back to shore. Once in, he was taken to hospital where it turned out that, after coming off of that wave, he had burst a blood vessel at the back of his heart.

It turned out that of the last two men missing, one, the Captain, was never found, and the other, the Chief Officer, was found dead on top of the breakwater the next day by the RAF helicopter.

The top wind speed was 128mph before the machine broke at Dover Coastguard station, and as we know this day is now remembered as 'The Hurricane of '87'. We were all awarded RNLI medals for this job, which were presented to us by Princess Alexandra at the Festival Hall in London.

The crew of that night were:

Roy, who is now Honorary Secretary at Dover Lifeboat.

Mick Abbott, who I'm afraid to say died a few years ago.

Geoff, who now lives in Perth, Australia.

Dom, who now lives in Spain.

Eric, who now lives in New Zealand.

Dave Moore, RNLI shore crew

Robert and myself, who still live in Dover.

I'm still involved with the Dover Lifeboat. We sort money we get from the liners that call here, especially Fred Olsen's who are very good to us, and also the Ferry companies at Dover, where again, P&O are also very good to us.

The Greatest Change in my Life

Going to sea would be a big change that happened to me. My first foreign port of call was Bermuda, then Nassau, Jamaica, then other Caribbean islands before going through the Panama Canal and down the West coast of South America.

You can't imagine the difference of Dover to all of these exotic places. At sixteen years old it was amazing. The world would never look the same again.

I had many adventures at sea. It was incredible to see all these different countries – Africa, Australia, New Zealand, Russia, all through the Mediterranean, South America, and many more, and I enjoyed every minute of it.

But the main change in my life was meeting Andrea, my wife, for the first time.

I was moving house to the same street she was in. She was sitting on her doorstep having a quiet cup of tea. I was in my friend's van moving stuff to my house. I shouted out, 'I will be down in a minute, put the kettle on!' I knew how to woo women!

It went from there. I had to do a bit of chasing but I got there in the end. One day, I was walking up the road with a bunch of daffodils in my hand and there were some of my mates up the road.

They shouted, 'Look who's got flowers!'

I said, 'They're not flowers, they're sweets', and I bit the tops off and ate them.

If it hadn't been for Andrea, I don't know where I would have been now... dead, probably. I had a wild lifestyle at sea, getting up to all sorts.

I took on three children, Mark, Tara and Jay, and then we had Ben together. They are all my children, all treated the same, and we have had a wonderful life together. Andrea and I have never argued (as she is always right). Joking aside, we just haven't.

My first love was the sea, but Andrea is my main love, and long may it continue. I have always looked after her and the family, but now that's changing, and they are having to look after me.

Donald, Mickey and Goofy

In 1986, I was acting Quartermaster (steering the ship) on the Townsend Thoresen ship, the European Trader. She was a freight vessel. We were on our way back to Dover from Zeebrugge. I was taking my break down in the mess room, when I got a call from the bridge to come back up, as there was something going on in the Channel I should know about.

When I got on the bridge, the chief mate called me over to a conversation going on on the VHF radio. I heard the name of my fishing boat, the Anna-Marie, being mentioned and another local boat called the Bella-Rye. Then I heard the Dover Lifeboat calling my boat up. All kinds of things went through my head, I couldn't think what could have happened.

I called my boat to find out what was going on. My mate Bob came on to say that apparently the Bella-Rye was taking in water and my boat went to their assistance, but when they were nearly there my boat blew a liner, which, in modern terms, meant that the piston stopped working, so they were dead in the water.

All of this was happening just on the shipping lane about six miles out of Dover, so as a last resort they called the lifeboat, much to the disgust of three of the lads aboard that day, which I will come to later.

The lifeboat was on its way to the scene. Upon getting to the sinking boat, the Bella-Rye, they put a salvage pump aboard and started getting the water down and trying to fix the leak. After stabilising the boat, they towed her to where my boat was, to take a line so they could tow her as well.

This is where the coxswain of the lifeboat, Tony Hawkins, got the shock of his life, as there, on my boat, were three of his regular crew, who hadn't told him they were going fishing that day and wouldn't be available for any lifeboat shouts, and with me at work as well he was four men down on his crew straight away.

The procedure is to take the names of the people you rescue for the RNLI records, so there was my mate Bob Duffield, Vic Naylor an old fishing friend, then Micky Mouse, Donald Duck and Goofy. Their real names were Geoff Buckland, radio operator on the lifeboat and two crew members Mick Abbott and Dave Austin. This was very embarrassing for them, as you can imagine they took a lot of stick for ages, plus it made the local press: 'Lifeboat crew rescued by their lifeboat' was the headline. We still have the cutting today.

I'm just glad I wasn't there as I would have had to have been Pluto that day.

Salvage of the Bleriot

Early one July morning in 1989 I got a call from the coastguard saying a plane had come down in the English Channel, and did I want to go out and get it? I thought, 'Why hasn't the lifeboat gone to it?'

The reason was because it was a Blériot plane ditched, the pilot was rescued, and the down draft from the helicopter sank the plane, so that as they flew away it appeared she had sunk without a trace. However, because she was made of wood, her tail fin came up above the water.

So, I made my way down to my boat and proceeded to go out to her last reported sighting near the South Goodwin Lightship. The sea was flat calm; a beautiful day for plane hunting, I thought. On my way I saw a yacht coming my way, so I went over to them and asked if they'd seen a plane floating about.

Well, you can guess the answer I got back, they thought I was mad. Off I went on my search.

Near the lightship I saw something sticking out of the water. Yes, it was the Blériot, so I went stern-to, so I could try to get a rope on her. I managed to put the rope through the tail section. Then, I tried to pull her aboard my boat, without much success, because the weight of the engine was keeping her down by the front of the plane.

I secured it as best I could and started to head for Dover. I had kept the coastguard informed of what was happening, and asked if the ferries would give me a wide berth as I didn't want their wash breaking the plane in half. But then, all of a sudden, I had helicopters above from the news stations, a local boat with the owner of the Bleriot on board, and other craft with film crews on.

There I was, plodding along, quite happy, singing 'I'm Popeye the Sailor Man,' when all hell breaks loose.

One of the owner's people came up behind me on a launch and jumped into the sea next to the plane. He was trying to cut the wings off, they said it didn't matter about those, it was the original engine and body that mattered.

I wasn't having any of that and told them to keep away and increased my speed a bit. Then, the owner, Mr Blériot, who was on the harbour launch came closer and wanted me to pass my rope over so they could get her on board their boat, as they had more manpower and didn't want her to get damaged.

As we were just off the port I agreed to do this (it *was* his plane). Anyway, they couldn't get it aboard, so they towed it instead.

Once near the slipway in the harbour, people got in the water and managed to drag it ashore. There were hundreds of people on the beach by this time because it was on the news channels and on radio.

I went and tied my boat up and made my way to the beach. I was swamped by the press and the TV wanting to do interviews. They were all saying 'You are going to be a millionaire!'. I wasn't bothered by all that, I just enjoyed going out and finding her and getting her back.

The next day, someone phoned my wife and said 'What's it like to be a millionaire?'

She said 'I don't know, but I'm kicking my hoover to make it work at the moment so I'm not too interested.' She put the phone down on them.

We were never millionaires, but we got a nice drink for my four hours' work salvaging the Blériot, and the nice thing was Mr Blériot got his plane back nearly in one piece - and I understand he still has it today.

What's in my pockets?

One week, Liz got us writing list poems. These are quick and easy - you just make a list! I listed the contents of my pockets. Surprising, how simple things like this can produce something interesting.

My dementia card, my little blue card (better than a passport),
My Galaxy S4: music player, message maker, *What's App?*
My blue shades,
My keys to my Yeti.
Pound coins, handy for the machine,
Two pound coins: less to carry around.
Five pound note: coffee and Panini.
Sixty pound in notes, soon to be gone.
I am Christopher William 'Battle of Jutland' Ryan.
These are the things I carry with me today.

Little Blue Card / Passport

I mentioned in my list poem, 'What's in my Pockets,' my 'little blue card, better than a passport.' I thought I'd better explain.

One morning, I was going on a day trip to France with some of the lifeboat old crew. We went through both French and English controls, without having to show my passport, and then again, I didn't show it at the ticket booth.

So, off to the ship we go, ready to sail to France, when I realise don't have my passport with me.

One of the lads said, 'Are you going back for it?'

I said, 'No, we'll get back in okay.'

We had our day out, and got back to the British Control at Calais. I handed three passports over, but the officer said 'There are four of you, where's the other passport?'

I said I had left mine at home, but I had my dementia card. He thought I was joking. I reassured him, 'No, I do have dementia.'

He checked the other passports and then called someone up. We were guided to another office where a man came out and looked at my dementia card, and asked me if I knew where my passport was.

I said, 'Still in the drawer, at home.'

He said, 'Ok - fill this form in, sign it, and you can go.'

How great was that?! The lads were amazed.

Wherever I go, I make sure my little blue card is always with me, as you never know when and where it might come in handy.

Description: Key Ring

It's square and smooth. It's getting jaded, very jaded. It has a ship on it and also the Merchant Navy flag, and a Merchant Navy emblem. It's plastic. A good friend of mine gave it to me. It's a key ring.

My key ring was given to me by an old seaman friend, who was a 'boy' rating in the Second World War. He was sunk three times by U-boats. The things he saw and went through were amazing.

The key ring shows the ship SS Athenia. She was the first ship sunk, within hours of the war starting. The U-boat U30 sank her.

By chance, there was a lot of ships about to help, and 981 people were rescued, but ninety-eight passengers and nineteen crew died. This was the first of many Merchant Navy losses throughout the war. Theirs was a very dangerous job. They kept the country going, bringing in supplies and food. Also, the Arctic convoys helped the Russians.

There is a Merchant Navy memorial at Aldgate in London, to all the lost seamen.

Speaking of lost seamen, I'd like to recommend a poem I recently read, called 'In Waters Deep,' by Eileen Mahoney. It means a lot to me, because my granddad's brother, Joseph Ryan, an Able Seaman at the Battle of Jutland, was on HMS Invincible in the First World War. She was sunk on May 31st 1916 with the loss of

1,026 lives. Only six men were rescued. He was drowned and lost at sea, so there was no grave.

My granddad, George Ryan, was on HMS Lion and saw his brother's ship hit and sunk. For all seamen and fisherman lost at sea, this is a very fitting poem.

Joseph Ryan was one of many who lost their lives in the First World War who was represented by one of the ceramic poppies in the 2014 display at the Tower of London.

My Old Cabin

In the cabin on my old ship, The Port New Plymouth, I made a double bunk out of a sheet of marine ply.

I got a double mattress off the purser out of a passenger cabin. I painted the cabin out and stuck some posters up.

I had a small cassette player up on a small shelf, a small wardrobe and two drawers under the bunk.

I never took a lot with me, no matter how long I was going away for. I only had two sets of gear to wear ashore.

I had a small bathroom cabinet, a little table and a daybed, all very cosy to spend months at sea in, then ready for the good times to be had in New Zealand and Australia.

So many good times – I could write a book!

Oh: I am writing a book!

There is Life After Diagnosis

After my diagnosis of fronto-temporal dementia, I thought we just had to get on with our lives and that's it. How wrong was I?!

After attending some coffee morning groups, which were not for me, I was invited to join the Forget-Me-Nots group in Canterbury.

This has opened a whole new life for me. At my first meeting I sat next to Reinhard, my Consultant Psychologist, and said to him, 'Who are all the doctors here?'

He said 'Only me and James, everyone else has a form of dementia.' I was amazed as the meeting was being run by all these people.

I thought Keith, who has Alzheimer's, was a doctor, because he was taking notes and was chairman of the meeting. He knew everything, and everyone else was giving their views about different subjects. This isn't the view of dementia that the public sees, or in my view, that the government sees.

So now I'm a member of this wonderful group, with so many great people. We really are a great mix, and we like to get everybody's view. This is very important as everyone's experience of dementia is different.

I have sat on interview panels for different grades to work with dementia, I have spoken at memory clinics about how I cope with living with dementia, and about what support is available. Also, I spoke at a conference in Ashford, Kent, with Lewis Slade, a Psychology Undergraduate about living with fronto-temporal dementia.

Later on, we spoke at a psychology conference in Shrewsbury (the 2014 Faculty of the Psychology of Older People Conference), to professors and clinical psychologists, and other people involved in working with dementia.

Our presentation won the award for the best presentation over the two day conference. I was so proud of Lewis for all the work and help he has put into me, and I know he will always remember that day on his rise to becoming a top psychologist!

I have written to the Prime Minister about getting a grant for everyone with a diagnosis of dementia so the government can pay for them to get Lasting Power of Attorney. This is something that you are told to do, because without it you can have all sorts of problems, with your finances, your wishes and your health.

Who would have thought it! Here is me with a diagnosis of dementia and I'm involved in all of these things.

Now, I know this might sound strange, but there are benefits to having dementia: all the work we are doing for the future for people with dementia, all the great people I have met in our group and at meetings and interviews; letting people know about dementia, and that it's not a death sentence, and that there are lots of things out there for you.

We can make a big difference to the people in power to learn from us, to make sure they are getting it right for the future of dementia. Also, for the carers there are plenty of groups and organisations to help them as well.

Lastly, things are changing for me, I know it. Certain things become more difficult. Simple things are not so easy anymore, but you have got to do your best to get on with your life as best as you can. My wife, Andrea, and I thought we would just carry on as normal, but as we now know that is not what happens.

We started on the same path, Andrea is still on that path, but I'm on the M25: normal; slow; fast; stop; let's get off. That's what it seems like to me. But, we shall carry on and see where it takes us.

Keith

To my wife, Rosemary;
for your love and support

Writing in this section was supported by Sophie

I'll never forget the time I went...

...to see the neurologist at the hospital on 5th May 2010.

The day began normally. The sun was shining. The BBC Breakfast weather girl predicted warm sunshine which pleased me as a trip in the sun is always better than in the rain. Dinner duty back at school awaited me, and it is much less hassle if the children are able to run around outside. Today, because it was so dry and warm would have the added bonus of them going on the field.

Rosemary and I arrived in good time. I hadn't been to this hospital before, so I was more nervous about being late, and not finding the right reception area rather than to receive the results of my MRI scan.

Why would I need an MRI scan if I had problems with my balance and ears? I only briefly dwelt upon this question.

I was relieved to be met by a friendly receptionist in a quiet waiting area. A promising start.

What time is it... 10:15 - my deputy would be standing in for me and conducting the assembly today. I did chat to her before leaving school last night and we agreed the story and the hymn - a story about being positive, and the hymn, well it was *'One more step around the world I go.'* That should go with a bounce as always, the children love that one.

Exactly on time the neurologist's nurse calls me in to have my weight and blood pressure checked. All very routine I'm assured.

Back into the waiting room.

Break time back at school now, again, thank goodness for the sunshine.

Thoughts of school were interrupted by 'Mr Oliver, will you please come this way.' I was led accompanied by Rosemary my wife, across the waiting area to a typical doctor's consultation room. Square. Modern. paperwork strewn across a table. Computer screen idling on the corner of a desk. NHS files much like the Department for Education equivalents in my office. And there centre stage was the neurologist who until this moment was merely a name on an appointment letter.

In the next few moments this was to change, but not only that, you could say my life was to change.

The consultant then asked us to take a seat and asked a series of questions about my health, why I had gone to my GP a month or so previously, to which I explained about the falls, the tiredness, the inability to concentrate, the *petite mal* type phases recently experienced. He listened intently to what seemed like a long explanation, but wasn't really. Then he embarked on a series of what I thought of as silly questions: what month is it, what season, who is the prime minister, count back from seventy in sevens - all very easy. Then onto him reading three words and asking me to repeat them - I hadn't a clue, where are we at this moment - can't remember the name of the hospital but I know the town, isn't that good enough? Then the three words/objects again - still they didn't register. This prompted him to pause and turn his, and then our attention to his computer screen.

'Well Mr Oliver, I think that the results of your scan and what you have said to me today is consistent with early stages of Alzheimer's Disease.'

He went on to say that the GP had referred me for the scan to rule out a brain tumour. He assured me there was no tumour. Along with Alzheimer's this was the first time this had been mentioned.

I was speechless. My wife was speechless. He sensed this, and went on to explain that this was a suggested diagnosis and lots more tests and scans would be required in order for this to be confirmed.

He then drew two helpful pictures, showing as he described it, a healthy fifty-four year old brain; and then he drew mine based on the scan - he did try and explain the scan to us but it was too difficult to draw sense from it. The comparisons the drawings illustrated were helpful then, and subsequently as we came to terms with this and tried to explain it to friends and family.

By now I was regaining some sense of the moment and the dialogue which was necessary I felt. The first question revolved around the subsequent tests and scans, then we moved on to talk about carrying on working which I wanted to do.

Next we raised the question of our forthcoming, long booked annual trip to Australia. We were alarmed by his response to this which was... not to go. *But everything is planned and paid for!* His advice remained the same.

Subsequently, I reflected upon this. Determined with Rosemary's support to go ahead with the trip, albeit with a slightly amended itinerary, I wrote to the neurologist to say I felt with us visiting friends and having been many times before the benefits far outweighed any potential risks. Thankfully, he was kind enough to send a written reply stating that if I felt well enough then I should go.

It left me though with the thought which I've never forgotten which is, had I taken his advice - as many would have done in that situation - we would have missed a wonderful trip which has subsequently been followed by four more trips to South Australia, our beloved place in the sun.

The sun was still shining as we emerged from the confines of the hospital. I suggested to Rosemary, 'Let's have a walk on the beach nearby' - a favourite spot of ours to clear our heads and take stock - 'And I'll ring school to get someone to cover my lunch duty.'

That's what we did, and I turned to Rosemary the moment we felt the sand under our feet, and I said, 'One door closes and one door will open.' I didn't know which door it would be, but I have been proved right.

Memories of my student days

A memory walk I've taken has allowed me to take time to think and reflect in, what with family events, dementia conferences and TV news interviews, has been a very hectic week. As I write this I have just arrived home from my weekly visit to a local primary school where I hear children aged eight and nine read, and have the thrill of reading their choice of book to them. I have just removed my iPod, and settled down to write...

Listening to music, especially through an iPod when walking rarely fails to transport me back in time to when either I first heard that song or album, or to a significant event in my life connected to the music. Or, maybe the music provokes a memory which is more tenuously associated altogether.

This morning the music ringing through my ears, and if I'm truthful prompting me to share my singing of (quietly, I might add) with passers-by, was that from the movie *Les Miserables*. A few days previously my wife and I really enjoyed going to see the movie at the cinema. Unlike millions of others we haven't seen the show - yet - and went only with an inkling of the story based on the plethora of reviews we have seen on TV recently. Often the music, the memories and the events of the day thread together and that was certainly the case today.

It was the rousing songs which transported me back in time to when as a student in the 1970s, I, like many, thought we could change the world, or at least have a positive impact upon it. A thread of this remains with me today.

As a student I was quite politically tuned in, and in my fresher week joined the University Labour Society. I was a moderate voice in a place where Marxists and Trotskyites often shouted loudest.

In 1975 we were frustrated that the political party we had elected had the temerity to try and introduce a series of spending cuts which targeted education. Do times change, I ask myself? To me Education was crucial as it had been my escape route from the council estate, from which I had different aspirations than the work in a factory or office which appeared to be on the cards.

A large group of us, I can't remember the number but probably in the region of sixty to seventy initially, decided to walk into the University administration building armed with our text books and sleeping bags in order to demonstrate our feelings.

The University authorities were sympathetic, after all this was the Socialist Republic of Sheffield at that time. We didn't quite blockade the doors but were left alone as long as we didn't wreck the place and dispersed after a few days.

Well, we attracted positive media and local attention! The TV filmed us and we had speakers who had escaped from Pinochet's military regime in Chile who came and inspired us with their true stories and songs which reflected their struggle. Local Labour MP for Heeley in Sheffield, Frank Hooley, came to speak with us. I remember him saying during a group conversation that I should be going into politics and not teaching: no thanks!

Richard Caborn who at the time was on the city council, and later became Sheffield's Euro MP and then MP in Parliament and a minister in Blair's government came to lend his support. A student friend who, unlike me, chose politics over teaching, later became his agent.

After about a week, with numbers dwindling after the initial flood of enthusiasm to a core of about twenty the demo concluded with a rousing finale as a coach-load of us joined the national campaign in marching through London to demand that the Government listened and changed direction.

Walking along the Ashford Road today with the rousing Les Mis I'm transported back to that march.

Whilst *I Dreamed a Dream* is one of my favourite songs from the film, the ones which most stir my emotions and transport me back in time to our student protest, whilst allowing me to sing along either in my head or if no one is around more vocally are *Red and Black*, *One More Day* and probably most emotive *Bring Him Home*.

Unlike the Parisians of 1848 portrayed in the film, we did walk home at the end of our protest. Seldom do I listen to these without a little lump in my throat.

I haven't thought about this period of my life for some time, and when I reflect I think about growing up in the 1960s, which were such interesting times to be influenced as an impressionable youngster.

The 1968 student unrest lit flames in Paris which almost ousted De Gaulle and threatened to sweep across Europe. The anti-Vietnam War movement was something which as a youngster I related to, views confirmed when in 2003 I was fortunate enough to visit the lovely country of Vietnam.

I find the music of that period still inspires me as it did as a teenager and as a student. Interesting to note that along with Les Mis from 2012 I have the music of Dylan, Tom Paxton and Pete Seeger from the 1960s on my iPod.

Time to reflect further. Was the experience and memory I've described a positive one? I think so. There are many parallels with this episode in my life and what I am attempting to achieve today with my voluntary role as Kent's Dementia Envoy.

Since those student days I have always done my best to help to make a difference, firstly as a relatively moderate, idealistic student, then as a primary school teacher who was committed to ensuring that the children in my care were well looked after and taught, then to a headteacher who strove to achieve a school learning experience in which all involved could be proud. Using this memory walk experience I'm convinced that there is a connection between each of these.

This piece began very differently as an original idea written over a year ago. Following suggestions from April Doyle during the Life Writing course I read *Dear Fatty* by Dawn French and this is my attempt to follow that thread. **This letter is dedicated to a person who has encouraged me to write and continue to teach, and who like many of you has inspired me so much by your faith and support. Thank you.**

Once a teacher, always a teacher

Dear former pupil,

As I sit at my desk pondering this letter to you, autumn is swiftly approaching, and is often regarded as a time for reflection as the vivid red, gold and orange foliage transforms the greens of summer to a hot flush before the winter chills set in. Whilst I do enjoy what this season provides, it is tinged with a little sadness as the realisation sinks in that summer has slipped away like the setting sun, and that one feels about to be gripped with a melancholic iron glove.

As a teacher and a head for over thirty years, early September also saw the end of the long summer break, and a return to life at school. Whilst I loved my time working with young people like you, I was always unsettled and anxious around the last days of the holiday, and remained so until the first day's register was marked, or the opening assembly of the year was completed. Then with your smiling faces in front of me I was comfortable casting off the mooring from the holiday and floating into the new term focusing on you, the most important people in my care.

Rewards from my career far outweigh what I contributed, and I don't mean financially. Although my salary latterly was far more than I could have imagined as a teenager leaving my Nottingham council estate, and I'm sure there were higher paid jobs out there than teaching, I always saw teaching as a vocation, and I never wavered from that throughout my career. Indeed you helped keep this as my focus. I am reminded of the wise words of Abraham Lincoln when writing to his child's teacher 150 years ago. These were shared with me by the parent of a pupil some years ago, whose view of the teacher he wanted for his child matched my attempts.

'Steer him away from envy and teach him the secret of quiet laughter.

Let him learn early that bullies are the easiest to lick.

Teach him the wonder of books. but also give him time to ponder the eternal mystery of birds in the sky, bees in the sun,

and flowers on the green hillside.

Teach him it is more honourable to fail than to cheat; to have faith in his own ideas, even if everyone tells him they are wrong and to be gentle with the gentle people and tough with the tough.

Give him the strength not to follow the crowd, to listen to all men but to filter all he hears and to take only the good which comes through.

Teach him to laugh when he is sad and that there is no

shame in tears. Teach him to scoff at cynics and to sell his brain to the highest bidder, but to never put a price on his heart or soul'

I do wish that the OFSTED Gestapo would read and digest these great words of wisdom - I did and tried to follow them, I hope that this came over to you when I was with you, if not then please accept my sincere apologies, I did try.

As a teacher and head one can make a real difference to the lives of young people, and I derive a great sense of pride and satisfaction every time the paths of a former pupil and myself cross. For you may be surprised, but in my mind you remain as a child, you have never aged or grown up in my memory. Childhood is a real treasure and these memories sit well alongside this.

There are so many of you I could write about, and thinking back to that first class, who I remember so vividly, despite the fact that it is now thirty-six years ago and many of you are parents yourself (some of you might even be grandparents!)

Soon after being diagnosed, my wife and I attended two meetings of people with a similar diagnosis. The meeting was designed to bring together those below the age of sixty-five who had recently been through the local Memory Clinic. The doctor setting up had an opening slide entitled *'Living with dementia'* by Dr Richard Brown. I said to Rosemary as quietly as I could, 'I taught a Richard Brown about twenty-five years ago in Canterbury. The last time I saw him he was eleven and moving on to Grammar School, I reckon he must be early to mid-thirties, about the age of this guy.'

The presenter overheard, and to my delight he announced, 'Yes, Mr Oliver, you DID teach me for two years and I remember with great fondness being in your class, including your great impression of Gollum when reading '*The Hobbit*' to us!'

Well, I was amazed. We chatted at length during the interval and I mentioned to Richard that I had a project he had written about Australia back in 1988. It was excellent, and I had 'borrowed' it to help inspire other subsequent children with writing their projects. At the next session I was able to ceremoniously return the project to rapturous applause from the group. Now the roles are reversed; I cared for Richard as his teacher, now as my consultant he cares for me. Thank you, Richard.

Soon after this, through a mutual friend in Australia, I made contact with Amanda who I had taught in Adelaide back in 1989. Amanda was by now a mum and a teacher herself, and indeed had taught in the UK and had tried, unsuccessfully at the time to contact me.

In October 2012 I had a meeting in London to train as a member of the Alzheimer's Society Research Network. Rosemary was going to attend this training with me and coincidentally Amanda, her husband and two young children were going to be in London that day. We had a lovely time together strolling along the South Bank near the London Eye before heading into a restaurant where the food was good and the conversation was great as we shared memories of the year we spent at Norwood Primary School in Adelaide.

I am delighted that so many of you have returned into my life recently, often in the most surprising of circumstances. In 'An Amazing Day' I have written about Amy who contacted BBC radio during the broadcast of my interview with the Prime Minister. Subsequently I am delighted that we have become friends, and as I write this we are planning to meet for the first time in over twenty years; oh how time moves so quickly!

An even longer gap was the case with Angela, who Rosemary and I recently met by chance at a party of a mutual friend. I hadn't seen Angela for over thirty years, and whilst we were enjoying the party we were getting ready to leave when Angela came up to introduce herself. Over an hour later we finally said our goodbyes!

Often former pupils will just stop and say hello in the street, and sometimes this leads to me asking what are you doing with yourself these days. One day in Canterbury, a young woman who was entertaining a growing crowd busking with her musical pals saw me, stopped her performance and came and took me to meet her friends, introducing me as her head teacher and saying lovely things about her time at Blean. If you read this Milly, you made that day for me and as I told you at the time, your music was brilliant.

Each September I am asked to deliver a talk to Occupational Therapy students at Canterbury Christ Church University, and at one of these talks a student came forward and introduced himself as Ben who I had taught almost twenty years previously. It was great to catch up and share what had led him to being on this course, and the work which he hoped to do once he had graduated.

Another opening line I hear from some of you is 'Are you Mr Oliver? You used to teach me'. As I previously mentioned, although my looks have changed since the time in question, the adult in front of me has changed much more. Sometimes this opening question will come from someone coming to do some work at my house, such as Wayne who works for British Gas and now services our gas boiler, or Thomas who was a lively nipper when I think of him as a ten year-old in my football team at Barton School, and who has grown into a burly six footer working with an electrical company.

One-off contacts are nice, but I really love the feeling I get when someone like you transforms in my mind from the primary school child to the adult who I am proud to say I taught and helped grow into the person who I'm delighted to re-connect with, and to not only talk about you the child, but as the adult you have become.

Once a teacher, always a teacher. I guess that label fits me to a tee. Since retiring I do miss the children from school, and to address this for the past three years I have been made extremely welcome at Wincheap Primary School, near to where I live in Canterbury.

I have loved hearing the children read, and have been boosted by the knowledge that I can still engage with young people and support both their learning and their developing confidence. I am a bit like a grandparent; I see them relatively briefly, make a fuss of them, enjoy their company and chats and then disappear until next time, usually the following week. I am told by the school, and my experience suggests, that I bring much to our time together, but rest assured I take far more away with me when I walk out of the school each time.

Once a teacher, always a teacher. So far this letter has been reflective and has looked back over the past; to close I would like to look to the present and the future. Maybe there is a link here to my efforts in the Dementia Envoy role. The work I did with you as your teacher was so important, and my current role is now important in a different, but parallel, way. I am committed to continuing to utilise any teaching skills I retain to raise awareness around living well with dementia and to challenge stereotypes and stigma. There are still talks to plan, audiences to speak to, and messages to convey, and as long as I am well enough and have the support I've been blessed with to date, I will continue to try to teach.

Thank you and bless you

Your teacher and friend,

Keith Oliver

I was very keen to lead a final assembly with the whole school at Blean School to say good-bye at the time of my retirement. I wrote this for the assembly, and read it alongside an interview written by Year 6 children.

A head's advice to his pupils

Always smile at those you meet
And they will do the same.
Look for good in others, dears
And don't waste time on blame.
Never be ashamed of crying,
It's not a sign you are weak,
And don't be quick to criticize
And think before you speak.
Always give more than you take,
Never do hurt nor harm
And don't be afraid of being wrong
If distressed, count to three and keep calm
Stick firmly to your principles,
Don't follow fads and trends,
And always listen to your heart
And value all your friends
Always refuse to give in
Aim for the stars and you might reach the moon
Enjoy time at home and at school
And always remember to sing a happy tune

An amazing day

Thursday 17th June 2014 was truly an amazing day.

The day began in bright sunshine with a freshly made juice and an inspired meeting with three wonderful, special young people who have become close friends over the past nine months.

These are psychology students from Kent University on placement with Kent & Medway Partnership Trust, and we have supported each other, and been inspired by each other on a number of projects. I'm absolutely delighted that we still have plans for future projects, amongst which are joint presentations this Autumn at an international conference in Glasgow and the UK Dementia Congress in Brighton this Autumn.

We also talk about lots of non-dementia subjects and that forms a substantial part of our time together and is the best help and support I could wish for.

Rosemary joined us just before noon, and the five of us together shared the experience of listening to the BBC Radio 4 programme 'You and Yours' which featured a piece with me recorded the previous day and a link to David Cameron, the Prime Minister, to whom I posed a question about dementia research.

I felt tense, waiting for the programme to start. My piece had been recorded the day before and I was very nervous (unusual for me - the hardest task usually at events these days is deciding which shirt to wear not the increasingly large audiences I seem to be speaking to!) I hadn't heard back my answers to the questions asked of me, and I had no idea what the PM would be asked or would say.

I thought David Cameron came across very well; sincere in his mission to make life better for those with dementia NOW and to put more money into this, and dedicated to finding a cure or other treatments/medication to arrest its progress. He made kind, specific reference to my answers and my approach to living as positively as possible with dementia.

I was most moved by a former pupil, who must now be in her early 30s, emailing/phoning the show live to express wonderful sentiments about her time in my class back in the 1990s. How I would love to thank Amy personally for this. Subsequently we are in email contact and will hopefully have met again by the time you are reading this piece.

Then the three students and I went into Canterbury for our sixth and final life writing class with eight people with dementia, our talented tutor, Liz, and our five patient and skilled student supporters.

This was a marvellous project funded partly by DEEP and partly by the Alzheimer's Society and we were very excited that it culminated in the publication of this book of our collected writings about our lives - something we are reliably informed has never been done by a group of people with dementia anywhere! Individuals have written their stories and groups have written for their own eyes but never in this way. We all hope that you are enjoying our efforts. Exciting!

When I got home and turned the computer on comments were starting to arrive from personal and professional friends about the programme. Whilst these comments mean so much to me personally, they really belong to so many other people who fight alongside me, those I know and those I have still to meet, all of whom are choosing to step through the door. I hope that by buying and reading this book, you can come through the door with us.

I've included some of the comments here, to share:

'You have reinforced the fact that there is so much more in your life than the dementia – you are a much loved father and grandfather; an 'interdependent' husband; a teacher; a writer; a campaigner; a football supporter; a friend; a student mentor. And in the way you approach all these roles and more, you are an inspiration to so many of us.'

'Keith, congratulations and well done, your commitment to bringing attention to dementia is outstanding, and I can see how it brings a more warm, positive approach/interaction with people who have dementia, as opposed to a purely negative medical response to the people who have dementia.'

'Well done. Thank you for the great work you have been doing to move the wellbeing agenda forward.'

'Please know that so many people are supporting you.'

Whilst these comments are wonderful to receive, the one received by text from my daughter was a marvellous conclusion that even England's defeat by Uruguay (in the World Cup) on the same day couldn't tarnish. Karon, my daughter told me that she and my grandson had heard the Radio 4 programme and that I was 'the best granddad in the world.' I ask for no more - and don't deserve that accolade - but I'll gratefully take it. It did make me cry like I hadn't for some time - tears of pride and joy.

As the day drew to a close, the sun was still shining and Rosemary and I sat in a reflective, relaxed mood, in our favourite spot on our patio with a cuppa and a biscuit looking out over the farmland, the meandering river and wild marshland which we are blessed to have next to our house.

I said on the programme, and on the day I was first tentatively diagnosed, one door closes and one door opens: there are many more doors for me to open in the future!

I wrote this on the second session of our Life Writing course. A Kenning is a poem of no more than eight lines, two words on a line and each line ends in 'er'.

Our cat Joshua: a Kenning Poem

People scratcher

Skilled hunter

Gift bringer

Occasional wanderer

Permanent dweller

Relaxed purrer

Plate licker

Rule setter

England win the World Cup, 1966

Every four years the nation seems to unite in hoping that our footballers will do themselves justice at the world cup, and this year is no exception. Writing this soon after England's narrow defeat against Italy, the pressure on the players seems to be mounting.

I suspect some of the reasons for this date back nearly fifty years to 30th July 1966, when Bobby Moore, as captain, held aloft the world cup trophy for the Wembley crowd to admire. Little would we imagine that all these years later no Englishman has repeated this act.

I was ten years old at the time and remember that warm, sunny day well. The nation had been gripped by football fever for three weeks with many matches broadcast in grainy black and white, not from the other side of the world but from places such as Liverpool and Sheffield. The world cup song and mascot was 'World Cup Willie' a lion dressed in the union jack with a jingoistic pop song to accompany his proud strutting around the TV adverts.

As always for me the day began with a bowl of cornflakes - I usually had them unless a cereal had a more tempting free gift lurking in the packet. The advantage of cornflakes was that their gift was often a figure to cut out from the outside of the packet so you could more easily collect the set. In 1966 it was famous people and the one I had to cut out and assemble that day was William Shakespeare.

After breakfast my mother could never keep me in the house.

I wanted to see my mates before the build up for the match. We usually headed for the wasteland near the local library where my mates and I had a den. We usually played war - TV and cinema films at that time were nearly all of the 'how we won the war' genre.

I can see us in my mind now, four or five ten year-old lads walking along carrying impressively real toy guns and rifles - mine was a Cowboy Winchester! Probably much imaginary blood was spilled and lives lost in the cause of our fun.

I remember a lad coming along named Clive who introduced himself as Clive, like 'Clive of India'. He was about our age, and I wonder how many ten year-olds on a council estate would introduce themselves as having the same name as an 18th century soldier today.

What we also did with Clive was swap Brooke Bond tea cards - Trees in Britain was the set at that time. I never saw Clive again but that has stuck in my memory.

I nearly always lost track of time when out with my mates but not this day. I was back home in good time to catch the pre match community singing of songs such as 'Abide with Me,' and the marching band of one of the guards regiments before the two captains proudly led their teams out of the Wembley tunnel to be greeted by a wave of noise never before seen or heard in a football stadium in this country.

The match; well, it ebbed and flowed. Geoff Hurst scored first for England, blond haired Haller equalised before Martin Peters leapt to head England back into the lead, and that is how it stayed until the last minute.

England-hearts sank when Weber poked in a late equaliser to extend the tension and take the game into extra time.

The crowd really got behind England as did my dad and I, shouting and cheering at the TV screen, hoping our support would make that little difference and encourage a winning goal.

It was only when West Ham favourite, Geoff Hurst fired the ball in off the cross bar - amidst much controversy - did the ball cross the line.

Dad got so excited he leapt up and crashed down, breaking the legs off the settee in the process: that goal resulted in us getting a new settee, thanks Geoff!

Soon after, Hurst broke free and scored the fourth goal - his hat-trick - and, as Ken Wolstenholm famously exclaimed, 'They think it's all over -it is now!'

My next memory of the match day is of Bobby Moore graciously wiping his hands before receiving the gleaming twelve inch trophy from the Queen and then holding it aloft. My mother who wasn't a football nut like dad and me, was really taken by a toothless Nobby Stiles dancing around the Wembley pitch clutching the cup.

Obviously I was too young to go into the pub - kids were very much barred from pubs in those days - but I remember my parents going down to the local to celebrate the world cup win, and the music which blared out into the car park where we kids kicked a ball around and relived the magic day. The music was the-then Number One, 'Out of Time' by Chris Farlowe, along with other recent hits such as 'Sunny Afternoon' by the Kinks and 'Get Away' by Georgie Fame.

A few bottles of dandelion and burdock later, I made my way home with my parents and started to think about what had been a very memorable day.

During the final Life Writing session Liz, our tutor set us the task in just a few minutes to create a 'list poem' by describing things which we had with us on that day, either in a handbag, a pocket or a carrier bag. We were directed to list out seven items and conclude the piece with the final two lines which Liz supplied, and we personalised by inserting our own name.

What's in my MAN bag

My brown leather wallet, stretched, not by money, but bulging with loyalty cards.
A brand new smart phone, looks impressive but am I smart enough to use it?
An old phone, a good old pal, but alas not smart enough.
Beautiful, sensitive music on a CD signed by Jennie, its talented creator.
In a case my glasses which, like me, respond well to the sun.
A pen to make reminder notes - my key to helping remember.
My diary, oh how I rely on you, my little red book.
My name is Keith Oliver
These are the things I carry today

In one life writing session, we viewed newsreel pieces from the late 50's and early 60's which prompted us write this piece. It was written as a collaboration between myself and psychology student, Sophie Razzel.

Gone too soon

Forever young
Stay that age, never allowed to grow old
Never seen them in the flesh, just an image or an icon,
The camera makes time stand still, captures a moment
Although the film fades, the memories remain
What could have been?

You were the people's princess and the queen of our hearts
No light shone brighter
Colours blurring;
Turning, turning

The paparazzi you courted were there at the end
The love you sought was there too, in the end
Beauty, glamour, vulnerability
Our image of you, with which we are left
We never met you, but we all felt we knew you
In life and in death
Elton's candle extinguished for the second time

Goodbye, Norma Jeane

The invisible child, the too-visible woman

Colours blurring,

Turning, turning

Forever viewed through the lens,

Lens of the kaleidoscope

Those eyes, the window to your true self, beyond the blonde hair

and smile

Childlike, but childless

The void in your life that fame could never fill

Puppet or puppeteer?

We took you seriously, Marilyn.

'Happy Birthday, Mr President'

Private lives, private affairs

Public death on our TV screens

Everyone remembers where they were when hearing the news

The images of the open top limousine

Your beautiful wife, in pink with that hat,

Delicately balanced.

The handsome, smiling president waving to adoring crowds

Except one person, lurking behind the sixth floor window

So much was promised from you and of you

KENNEDY ASSASSINATED

Colours blurring
Turning, turning

Young forever, somehow
Time moves on
Not with you, but not without you
Mystery muddies the water

The film fades, the memories remain
Gone too soon:
Colours blurring
Turning, turning.

Truth can be funnier than fiction...

The inspiration for this piece is multi-faceted. Firstly the notes were scribbled on a notepad zooming through the French countryside *en route* in the Eurostar from Ashford to Avignon. I find the northern French countryside less attractive than that below Lyon, consequently my mind wandering was more fruitful at this time. Allied to this I was reading David Sedaris and Jennifer Saunders. To Sedaris, I attribute the desire to embarrass my family, and to Jennifer my thanks for inspiring any humour you may detect in the words that follow.

French Connections

My first trip across the channel was with two other mates, soon after graduating from University, and we blew the proceeds of a holiday job in buying two tents and a Eurorail card to explore La Belle France.

We decided to pass through Paris and make for Biarritz as we had heard there was great surf there, good camp-sites and warm weather, and then to follow this by moving across to the Med and staying just outside Paris on the way back.

Loaded with tents and large rucksacks we pulled into Gare du Nord, and - to save a few francs - decided to walk across the city to Gare d'Austerlitz.

Little did we know the route would take us through La Pigalle which in those days made Soho look like a church picnic.

Despite living close to the red light area of Sheffield as a student, I saw sights that night that appear in no tourist guide, and I hadn't seen before or since. I am pretty sure that the ladies of the night realised we weren't interested. The only new experience I was tempted by that evening was a donor kebab, which I did indulge in for the first and only time in my life.

Once we arrived in sunny and breezy Biarritz and had pitched our tents, like all good Englishmen we needed to put the kettle on the primus. Directly opposite us were three French girls who were about our age, and were clearly using us as their source of entertainment. *No not that at La Pigalle and not here!*

They were obviously chatting about us and didn't realise that Dave was a fluent French speaker and qualified to teach French, and unbeknown to them he understood every word. He let them go on for ages and discretely relayed to us that they were saying *'the English are having their tea!'* before breaking the ice and revealing his linguistic talent. Well, as you can imagine their red sun tanned faces went several shades brighter after this revelation!

My dad - the fussy eater

Staying with a continental theme, my father hated foreign food. In fact, he wouldn't even refer to it as food, calling it *'foreign muck,'* although a favourite flan was in his words *'Quick Lorraine.'* I never did discover who she was!

Speaking volumes

My favourite shops are book shops. I just love browsing in them, buying books for myself and for others.

Rosemary went through a phase of enjoying books set in the wildlife parks of southern Africa and, after reading a review, asked me if I could buy 'Last of the Free' by Gareth Patterson for her birthday. I was happy to have a suggestion to assist with present buying, so went into my local bookshop a few days later.

It wasn't on the shelves so I went to the counter and told the young assistant the title of the volume I was after. After some typing into the computer, his expression became at first puzzled and then a bit alarmed. A queue was beginning to form behind me when he said, 'I'm sorry sir this book doesn't appear to exist on our system.'

'I'm sure it does,' I replied, 'we read a really positive review in Saturday's Daily Mail.'

To which he turned his computer screen in my direction and said 'There is no book, sir, called Lust for Free.' He showed me the books he had been searching amongst, and I was shocked by the range of 'adult' titles there in front of me. No wonder he was alarmed. I was as well, and embarrassed.

I glanced nervously over my shoulder at the growing queue hoping that no one else could see the screen. After a quick excuse (based upon my northern accent) the correct title was bought, ordered, purchased and read!

Artistic expression

Rosemary is a very good artist, indeed I would describe her as talented and, although extremely modest about her abilities, some of our favourite pieces enhance our walls at home.

In order for them to be hung they needed to be framed, and in Ian we have a picture framer who we know well and trust. Fortunately he knows us well and knows that we are inclined towards 'senior moments' on occasions.

One such occasion involved a phone call Rosemary made to him about wanting to frame her latest piece. Ian needing to know the orientation of the piece asked her if it was 'landscape or portrait' to which Rosemary in her naivety replied, 'No - it's a dog'. I'm pretty sure that wasn't the response he expected, and much laughter ensued.

Just William

Our grandson, William, is our youngest family member. He's six at the time of writing, and attends the same first school where his mum Karon is deputy head. William is a very bright boy with a very sharp sense of humour, but on this occasion I'm not sure that this prompted this story.

Karon asked him one day when he had not long started school, how the day had gone. Like most children he wasn't terribly forthcoming but did say he enjoyed going into the cold drinks room.

This puzzled Karon who said, 'We don't have a cold drinks room William,' to which he replied, 'Yes we do, it's the ICT room' - read it aloud and you'll see the humour!

The unfortunate metaphor of metamorphosis

Gareth, our eldest son, has worked in Insurance since leaving University and had done so with the same company for a number of years without seeking any substantial promotion. He is a shy, reserved chap who appears quite laid back.

A few years ago his company was putting together a special team to develop a project and internally advertised for members including someone with a creative background. This appealed greatly to Gareth who had an art degree and was, I guess, a bit frustrated that his considerable artistic skills hadn't been utilised during his work, so he applied and was interviewed.

At the interview he was very nervous, and to lessen his nerves he prepared answers in his mind beforehand. Anticipating the question why hadn't he pushed himself forward previously either in the company or through a move elsewhere, he came up with what he thought would be the perfect answer: the visual image of a beautiful butterfly emerging from a chrysalis. Unfortunately, his nerves sabotaged this answer.

Gareth managed to express the first part as intended before his nerves kicked in and he concluded the answer with feeling that this was 'An opportunity to emerge like a butterfly from a clitoris!'

Memorable I'm sure for the interview panel, and - yes - he not only got the job, but he simultaneously gave us one of our best ever family stories!

School of life

Teaching was a wonderful career to have and has left me with some fabulous memories: some serious, some sad, and some very funny. One I retold at an Alzheimer's Society Christmas Carol Service in London when re-telling a story from a Christmas card from a lovely Year 6 child named Kirsty, which read, 'To Mr Oliver, the best teacher in the world,' she should have stopped there but she went on to write 'You teached me good.'

I considered attaching that to my next job application, but thought better of it!

Early in my career I taught in Crewe for a short time and had a very difficult class with equally difficult parents, one of whom came to see me at Parent's Evening - this in itself was cause for celebration - but this mother came with the biggest badge I can remember proudly advertising 'I love sex and darts' (I'm not sure in which order!)

A week or two later she also wrote to me about Christopher, her son, who had been absent for a day with according to her scribbled letter diarhere, diarear, and, finally, *the shits,* plainly written.

Only in Canterbury

Also around that time I was new to the school and getting to know the children and the parents. I was meeting the parents of a Year 6 boy to discuss their choices for potential secondary schools. One popular choice in Canterbury is the Archbishops Church of England School, which is always quite difficult to get into, and clearly was their first choice.

I went into detail at some length about the difficulty of getting a place, to which they gradually got more and more jovial and animated which rather surprised me and caused me to say please let me in on the joke which was clearly developing at my expense. I genuinely didn't know what the source of their merriment was. To put me in the picture the mother said "I don't think that will be a problem as the Archbishop is his grandfather and my dad!' Needless to say that is where Archbishop Carey's grandson went.

Humour builds resiliance, positivity and, consequently, better health. People who retain a sense of humour are better able to deal with adversity and problems.

I think it's crucial to understand that, whilst humour cannot provide a cure, or the answers to our desire to keep dementia at bay, it certainly helps deal with the challenges that it presents.

Further anecdotes from Keith's life to make you chuckle are contained within our volume of additional writings, Life Goes On, *available as a free Kindle download from Amazon.com - Ed.*

The rich reservoir of travel

Travel so enriches one's life. Along with Australia, in the last couple of years we have travelled on the Eurostar to Avignon, taken an autumn break on the alluring Amalfi coast and spent a sunny week in June in Menton in southern France, alongside a first visit to Scotland at the age of fifty-five. All of these have added to my rich reservoir of holiday experiences.

Whilst the memory of what I did, said and thought is perhaps not as clear in my mind as I would wish, the overall feeling of positivity and well-being accrued from these trips lasts long after the cases are unpacked and consigned to the loft, until the next one.

Other memorable holidays Rosemary and I have enjoyed include twice going to Paphos in Cyprus which we did really like, and during one of these holidays we took a day trip to Cairo, yes Cairo! Bonkers, I know, but a great experience!

We flew from Paphos early in the morning and arrived in Cairo to be greeted by a coach with its own armed guard, as at that time there had been some disturbances where tourists had been targeted. After a first stop at a rather formidably beautiful mosque, we headed for the pyramids.

I remember looking in one direction and all you could see beyond the three pyramids (one of which was that of Cheops who I remembered learning about when I was about twelve) was a vast expanse of the Sahara desert, and then, turning around, one saw dilapidated, unfinished high rise flats marking the outer suburbs of

Cairo.

I managed to crawl through various tunnels in the heat of the day to reach the centre of the one open pyramid, only to be disappointed by merely an empty chamber - I guess I expected more from watching the *Indiana Jones* movies.

The treasures of the pyramids had been removed to the main museum in the city and that was our next stop (after a lovely lunch in a hotel nearby) where we had a couple of hours enthralled and entranced by the rich treasures on display, the highlights of which for us were those associated with Tutankhamen. Never have we seen anything so impressively crafted, with such rich materials and gold in abundance.

From the past to the present our next stop on the whistle stop tour was to be jostled and squashed in a very busy bazaar area where everyone seemed out to convince us that what they were selling was special and worth buying. We weren't tempted other than a couple of papyrus book-marks which I still have somewhere tucked away in a drawer.

After this a sit-down was needed, and we made for a boat trip on the Nile where a show was put on for everyone's entertainment - the highlight of which was a rather glamorous belly dancer, who performed whilst we were eating (maybe to encourage us not to eat too much in order not to expand our waist-lines!) After this we were whisked back to the airport for a late night flight back to Paphos, tired but buoyed by the memories of a wonderfully inspiring day.

Vietnam

No one could have escaped the images back in the 1960s of the Vietnam war, it seemed to be on the news every evening; more shooting, more napalm, more tears, more protests. To my generation Vietnam was associated with all of this, and consequently fascinated me as I sensed the country had much more to offer. Then in 2002 a parent at my school put me in touch with the Christina Nobel Foundation and we sponsored a child named Liem.

At the time, Liem was aged ten and lived a very basic existence in a small village just outside Ho Chi Minh city with his blind mother. We would receive a report from the Foundation every so often and I was keen to go and visit Vietnam and to see Liem and take gifts from our school community.

A year later, in April 2003, Rosemary and I made the trip and with the assistance of Thai Airlines took boxes of gifts, such as pencils, crayons, toothpaste and some new clothes - tee shirts mainly - from the school and Marks & Spencers who supported us.

From the outside, the charities administration building where we met Liem with his mother and staff from the charity was quite run down, like so much of that area of the city away from the tourist trails. Clearly he was nervous, as indeed were we, but with the patient reassurance from the Foundation staff, who acted as interpreters, we had a lovely hour or so together. The teacher translated and gifts were exchanged - he crafted us a lovely table and set of chairs from beer cans - I guess this skill was learnt in order to sell the items. This was very touching, and had clearly taken him a lot of time to make. For many years afterwards his gift was proudly displayed in a special glass cabinet outside of my school office for the children and visitors to admire.

Liem also shyly sang for us, an old Vietnamese folk song, which I was able to video to show the children back in England. Marlene (my deputy from school) had bought him a watch which he was so proud to wear, and he constantly kept looking at it almost in total disbelief.

One other lasting impression I had was that despite being so very poor, (Liem and his mother lived in a small hut made of mud and wood, with a coconut tree outside which they proudly told us provided them with food (the flesh), drink (the milk) and fuel (the shells)), they were both very clean, and Liem would not have looked out of place in his M&S 'Beckham' tee shirt back at Blean school in Kent.

We continued to sponsor Liem right through his education into Secondary school, including sending the money for the purchase of a bike to enable him to travel from his tiny hamlet to his secondary school several miles away. Contact did diminish as he moved into his teens. A bit inevitable I guess. The children at Blean saw him as one of our school and I do often wonder how he got on and what he is doing now.

This piece was written after the writing course with the support of psychology student, Sophie Razzel, and my wife Rosemary. It was inspired by a desire to share some experiences of past travels, and to maybe inspire future ones by myself and others.

Travel writing - Australia

A desire to travel and a love of visiting new places so enriches one's experience of life. I have always enjoyed visiting new places and re-visiting some old favourites. I suspect my love for this was nurtured as a child in the 1960s, when my parents chose to spend what little money we had on annual holidays. We alternated between an English south coast and joining the exodus of sun worshippers heading south to the Spanish costas, Jersey and the Austrian Tyrol, where we searched the hills which were promised to be alive with the sound of music.

This is one reason why I was so upset when advised to cancel our annual trip to Australia (see piece entitled 'I'll never forget the time I went...') by the neurologist on the day it was suggested that I had dementia. Whilst dementia does present certain challenges to overcome, it is still possible to safely and comfortably travel.

The way we recall and engage with our memories of past holidays is rather like the way we do with favourite pieces of music: both have the power to transport us to a past time and place, and enrich the present moment by exercising our memory. One should never under-estimate the benefits one can gain from a good holiday and the excitement, feel-good factor and interest which it often brings to the traveller.

Since our year in Australia in 1989, when I did a teacher exchange and lived in Adelaide, we have re-visited many times, and have been fortunate enough to have some wonderful memories with our Aussie mates and to have travelled extensively in this vast country. You can never see all of a country this size.

Adelaide is like a second home to us, and is a wonderfully laid back, beautiful city with a vibrant cultural scene, great beaches and wonderful hills overlooking the modern city which, until the late 1830s, was bushland, swamp and scrub. Beyond Adelaide there are the wine regions of the Barossa and McLaren Vale where the sun-kissed grapes make great red and white wine, needless to say we have many favourites for medicinal purposes, of course! Hahndorf, a small piece of Germany transported across the world to South Australia is a favourite destination of ours about forty minutes' drive out of Adelaide, where we can browse shops, cafes and restaurants, and even call into a German pub for a stein of ice cold beer.

Moving east from Adelaide, although not so keen on Melbourne, (it reminded me of Manchester with sunshine), rural Victoria has some spectacular coastal scenery along the Great Ocean Road and some classic Aussie rural scenery with sheep farms, sheep farms and more sheep farms. I love the sun-burned country.

Sydney became one of our favourite Australian places we've visited, where we enjoyed the beauty of the harbour and the iconic opera house and 'coat hanger' bridge and 'tuned into' the pace and buzz of a wonderfully vibrant, beautiful place to visit.

North to Queensland which in the dry season is a world away from one's experience in Europe - the Barrier Reef for all its problems is still as the name suggests - Great. Whilst on the reef Rosemary hired an underwater camera and took some great photos whilst snorkelling and James and I went fishing, returning our catch to the turquoise waters.

Although the towns of Cairns and Townsville are worth seeing, the highlight for us was a week spent on Magnetic Island, a thirty-minute ferry trip from Townsville. The island is a tropical paradise, named by Captain Cook due to the disturbance caused to his ship's compass.

Staying tropical, but moving into the Northern Territory. Darwin is a great location to do the 'Crocodile Dundee' experience and we did, spending five days out in the bush with the crocodiles learning to identify the difference between the 'salties' which would eat you and the 'freshies' which wouldn't - I think I learnt this!

Rosemary also had the bravery to ride on the back of Charlie the water buffalo, made famous for being hypnotised by Crocodile Dundee in that hilarious first film.

Next stop, Perth. The capital of Western Australia reminds me of Adelaide: modern, well planned with beautiful beaches and the added benefit of the Swan River and the manicured Kings Park looming majestically over the city. Perth is, though, more isolated from the rest of Australia and is closer geographically (and some would say economically and culturally) to Singapore than it is to

Sydney.

So far, like most Australians, we've stuck to the coastal fringe, it's now time to move inland to explore what's commonly known as The Outback.

Alice Springs, known as the capital of The Outback, has grown in size and stature between our first visit in 1989 and our return in 2010 without losing the feel of a town on the edge of the desert. In 1989 we were viewing the town as part of a large group of teachers and families spending two weeks in the outback visiting incredible places such as Coober Pedy, 846 kilometers north of Adelaide. Coober Pedy means 'White Man's Hole' in aboriginal, and is there because of the opal mines which dominate the area. This was our first night and was spent in a motel underground.

Most of the accommodation in the town is underground, as indeed are the two town churches. One building above ground was the supermarket and I remember seeing for sale in there dynamite along with the cereals and washing up liquid. Very useful.

At that time, a popular film was 'A Cry in the Dark', starring Meryl Streep as Lindy Chamberlain. This was the story of her losing her baby to a dingo while camping near Uluru. We visited Uluru, to photograph it at sunset, to walk around it during the day and to climb it. The ascent is steep and arduous and was too much for six year-old James who, unsurprisingly, found the hike up too challenging. Fortunately a stranger who was descending as we were ascending, offered to take him and look after him while we continued the climb, an offer we gratefully accepted. An hour and a half later, the family was reunited and all was well. Not a dingo in sight.

Moving forwards to 2010, and our next visit to The Outback was for a three day stop in Alice Springs, whilst taking the Ghan train from Darwin right across Australia, north to south, to Adelaide.

The Ghan is one of the world's iconic railway journeys, travelling 2720 km and taking nearly three days to complete if you were inclined to do it in one stint. Far better to do as we did, and break the journey in the middle in Alice Springs.

Building the railway from Adelaide to Alice Springs was a long and painful process taking from 1879 -1929 and named after the Afghans who helped, with their camels who carried the heavy equipment used to build it. (Subsequently the camels were released and formed a population larger than that in Saudi Arabia!) The portion from Alice to Darwin wasn't completed until 2004 - this after a three year building programme.

There are four standards of travel, red - you get a seat, silver gives you a bed and shared facilities, gold (which is how we travelled) gives you your own compartment with bunk beds and its own small but cosy toilet and shower and some great meals, and then there is platinum, which gives even more salubrious four star hotel style sleeping accommodation on the train.

The journey was fascinating, and to travel day and night on a train was a new experience to us. Each meal time you would sit with a different couple of people and engage - as is usually the case where Aussies are concerned - with some great conversation. Although not spectacular the scenery is fascinating and illustrated again the vast emptiness and rugged beauty of the outback. Again this experience would have been missed had I taken the professional medical advice.

Since being diagnosed, we haven't ventured outside of South Australia (SA) feeling that it was much easier - and just as fulfilling - to spend time in a place we know quite well, often, with friends whose company we love. This is not a negative at all as SA has so much to offer for a four week stay, and swapping the Pommie winter for an SA summer is a pretty good deal.

Had I taken the advice of the neurologist back in 2010, I would have missed out on so much. That said, we have made adaptations to allow us to enjoy future trips and I would like to share these suggestions in the hope that this advice encourages other people with a similar diagnosis to consider ways of facilitating enjoyable and safe travel.

Key principle: allow ample time- travel can be very tiring but VERY enjoyable!

- Travel with another person insurance/companionship/shared experience at the time and afterwards - laying down memories.
- Travel Insurance – be honest with companies, most will cover single trips for those with dementia.
- When making the booking discuss this with a doctor sharing your care. A letter from your GP regarding the medication you're carrying is advisable. In some cases a supporting letter

from a consultant might be helpful.

- Think carefully about the place you intend to visit – is it busy/quiet – crowds can be difficult: do you know the area? I like to go to a mix of the new and the familiar. The itinerary – best not to plan too much and consider rest days as well as active ones. Check that you have sufficient medication for the whole visit, plus a few days' extra in case of delayed flights/ travel. I would strongly advise that your medication goes in your hand luggage rather than in the hold - you have it with you, and it will not get lost.
- Help from tour operator with online seat allocation both in the UK and when confirming for return – this is usually 24-48 hours prior to departure
- Making check-in staff aware at the airport– enlisting their help through customs and security by:-
- Requesting early boarding of aircraft which usually means sitting in a specific area at the departure gate.
- Ensuring they make cabin crew aware – ideally this can be done via the tour operator when booking the flight/holiday. They will remind you of medication if required.
- Use of MAAS badge (Meet and Assist Service) to help with luggage retrieval and customs if required upon return to UK.

All of the above can easily be discretely and sensitively achieved with no fuss or embarrassment to ensure that travel is as stress-free and enjoyable as possible despite the difficulties which conditions such as dementia can present.

I would strongly recommend that you consult the following very helpful Alzheimer's Society factsheet number 474 entitled 'Travelling and going on holiday', available from: alzheimers.org.uk/factsheet/474

M. J. Saints

To my family, past, present and future

Writing in this section was supported by Jennie

Miss Mary Leigh

On days when my dementia is stronger and I can't get the most basic words, I get very anxious and all I want is to get back to the time when, as a child, I believed that dogs barked, cats meowed and human beings spoke my mother language. How it all was so simple then.

My father had explained to me that in other countries people spoke other languages, but only when I was eleven and at school starting to learn French was I confronted with the evidence that in France they spoke French, and, two years later, that in England they spoke English.

For a further four years my school friends and I were drilled in both grammars, and then if we had shown any promise we would have another two years to learn how to translate into those languages. But I have always thought that speaking a foreign language is a very difficult process. I used to think of it as working on a trapeze without a safety net.

You have to leave the emotional comfort zone of your mother tongue to this other world of strange sounds. Your ears and your vocal cords are not used to these new sounds. Your brain has to cope with a new syntax and a different way to see and describe yourself and the world around you.

I was very lucky to have been taught by excellent teachers who were able to make me relax and not feel like a fool. Miss Mary Leigh was the one for my last two years, and she was formidable.

She was imposing to look at because of her height and her hair colour. She was very tall with wide shoulders and big bones. Her hair, which she wore long and loose, was thick and red.

She dressed very well, I thought. Her clothes were plain, functional, and of very good material and cut. Tweed trousers and skirts with sweaters in winter and simple cotton dresses and skirts in summer. Not mannish. She was a very liberated woman who lived alone in a foreign country and did what she liked.

The only things out of character were the chiffon scarves and a Victorian ring she wore on her left hand. It had an amethyst surrounded by seed pearls. It looked incongruous: too dainty on her large hands. She used to fiddle with it all the time. I remember that because I would lose concentration watching her turn it round and round with her right thumb and forefinger.

On her first class she told us that English was a common sense language with plain, serviceable words.

'No Latin frippery,' she would say. 'Spare me of too many adjectives and adverbs. Never say you are absolutely terrified, if you are bloody terrified you don't need an 'absolutely'.

So, *what was bloody?* we all wondered, but couldn't ask because we were all terrified. However, from then on, 'bloody' because my favourite adjective in the English language.

'Never use Sunday words, pedantic words: I hear them everyday,' she loved to say. 'Just stick to plain language, come to the point, it will serve you well.'

Not one of us dared point out to her that a week without a Sunday was a very sad thing. She would have said, 'For goodness sake, don't be boring!'

The last time I saw her, she had summoned me for dinner at her favourite restaurant.

We were both much older. She was over eighty, a bit shorter in height, her hair no longer on fire but more like pale straw, and she used to walking sticks.

I told her how I used to think that learning a foreign language was like working on a trapeze without a safety net, but that she had been always there for me. I thanked her for it.

'Well, you weren't that bad, you know,' she said, while asking the waiter for another bottle of her favourite Douro wine.

Now, on foggy brain days, I wish I could tell her that I want to go back to when I only knew one language, not four.

I can hear her saying, 'Don't be silly! Keep on!'

Yes, Miss Mary Leigh; I'll try for you.

Letter to Robert

Your father and I went to the beach yesterday. It was a very hot day and we sat by some rocks under an umbrella. The smell of the sea. Made stronger by the proximity of the rocks, reminded me of our days at the beach when you were two, and I was thirty.

We used to arrive at ten, when the sun hadn't made the sand too hot to walk on bare feet. We would drop the straw bag with the towels, buckets, spades and sun lotion on the sand.

You were always so eager to get the buckets and spades out of the bag. Your bucket was bright red with blue boats and white sails. It matched your red hat perfectly. Next I would cover you in suntan lotion. You were then ready for a day of serious work.

Castle building with sand requires concentration. You can't use sand either too dry or too wet. It has to have just the right wetness. If too dry it runs through your fingers, and if too wet it becomes a gritty liquid that doesn't hold its shape.

So we would look for the strip of beach that the tide could barely reach, and that the sun was starting to warm up. There the best sand could be found. You would fill your bucket, then we would press the sand down to get rid of the excess water. I would help you to turn the bucket upside down and the material for starting the walls of our caste was ready. Your little hands would press it into shapes that sand castle architects recommend as sturdy and firm for castle walls.

We would get very hot as the building progressed, so when we would hear the swish of the tide coming close we would wait for the cool water to freshen our hands so we could keep up with our building. When the last wall was finished we would smooth the whole castle gently so that it wouldn't fall down. Because we didn't want it to dry out, we would cover it with the sea shells we had collected.

There it stood all white and sand colour against the green sea. You would clap your hands and call Claudia to see your splendid castle. She would call back from the water, where she was splashing about with her friends, saying how great your castle was. We would then stand back on the dry sand under the canvas shade because by then the sun would be high and the sand too hot under our feet.

Sitting down later on the soft towels, looking at the sky so blue, the sea so green, both contrasting with the white sand, our castle made of sand and sea, looked part of it all. And so did you, with your shrieks of delight.

With a big hug from,
Your Mother

My 40th Birthday

My daughter, Claudia, was sixteen and we were coming to Europe from New Zealand.

Claudia asked the very nice Singapore Air hostess, 'Could we have some champagne? Today is my mother's fortieth birthday.'

I told Claudia they don't give champagne in Economy.

But they did!

We had a lovely flight. Paris looked even more beautiful than I remembered, if that were possible, when we arrived. Eighteen years earlier, my husband and I had spent our honeymoon there.

Another present on my 40th was going to the Louvre and watching Claudia's face when she saw the Olympia of Manet. She had been studying Manet for her Art History exam and there it was!

'Oh my God, it is so much better than in the book,' she said.

Her sixteen year-old eyes couldn't believe in what she was seeing, neither could mine looking at hers.

Such a long time ago, but just like yesterday...

Farrusca

Farrusca and her sisters and brothers were born under our house in Auckland in New Zealand.

Her mother was feral, and nobody could go near her kittens. Eventually, she moved them to the storage space above our garage and my brave husband began a relationship with them, despite all the hissing and spitting.

As time passed, they began to feel at home with us.

Our children loved them all, but we couldn't keep so many kittens. We distributed them among our friends and felt very sad for a long time.

We kept Farrusca, because she was shy and beautiful. She was a very elegant grey with the most striking green-yellow eyes. She was the most gentle cat I have ever known.

Her world was in the garden where she enjoyed the sun, slept, and spent her time climbing up trees and scaring the singing birds.

In the evening she loved watching television on the lap of one of the children.

Sometimes, first thing in the morning, she would bring us a dead mouse, so that we   much she loved us.

She was a cat, afte   thought of her as our child or sister.

I'll Never Forget...

I'll never forget the 17th of January, 1966. The portrait painter came to deliver the portrait of Mrs. Morris.

It was a rainy day, and he wore a grey raincoat over a sage green sweater that his mother had knitted. He introduced himself.

'I'm David Steel, the portrait painter who has been painting Mrs. Morris. She told me about you.'

'Oh,' I said, 'I'm Maria Joana Castro de Gama, and I'm the *au pair.*'

God! I thought, *He is very good looking!*

And that was how I met the man who would be my children's father.

Memories of long-ago afternoons

I remember afternoons at the house of my great grandmother and grandmother, when they would have friends for coffee while chatting and embroidering, knitting and crocheting.

I was about six years old then, but my memory of those afternoons has never faded.

My great grandmother taught me to knit with brass needles and black wool, while my grandmother showed me how to crochet with white cotton and a bone hook.

I can still hear the sound of the brass knitting the black wool. I can't remember what they said, but I remember the sound of their voices and the smell of black coffee.

They died a long time ago, but what they taught me hasn't gone, and even in days of thick brain 'fog' I can use my hands, make something and feel creative and alive, thanks to those great ladies.

So when I sewed the ribbons onto the hat of my granddaughter Sadie, to protect her from the Sydney sun, I thought: she will pass it on to her sister Frida, and in years to come they will also remember me for that hat.

Changes

I arrived for the first time in London in the October of 1965. My father wouldn't allow me to come to England, so I had to wait until I was twenty-one to get a passport.

The day when I left my capital city was a bright day and that beautiful city was truly the City of Light.

When the plane landed at Heathrow, the captain said in our language, 'Thank you for flying with us. The temperature in London is nine degrees and there is a light rain.' Some guitar music followed.

For a few moments I thought I wanted to go back, but I didn't.

In the London of the '60s, I became an *au pair* in Belgravia. At the language school I went to, other girls my age from Germany, Austria, Italy, Spain and France became my friends.

Because we didn't have much money, we used to go to a Lyons' Corner coffee place. We complained about the coffee, but we all in our different accents agreed that we loved London.

Coming from a small town - where everybody knew who my father, my uncles and the rest of the family was - for the first time, I was anonymous. Just me, I was.

I still love London, which made me free and the owner of myself.

Letter to Sadie on her Third Birthday

On the next 25th of September you will be three-years-old.

I remember the time we went to Sydney for your first birthday. Then you were the loveliest and most beautiful baby girl. What a joy it was to be with you!

Your grandfather and I used to walk to Redfern Park with you in your buggy. I still can see your little red shoes going up and down with the excitement of soon going on the swings and slides at the approaching park.

You were so happy!

One year later we would do the same walk but by then we would collect twigs from the park's many trees, so that we could make little houses that brought smiles to your beautiful face.

But by then you were two years old and could run like a little rabbit, chasing the Ibis birds that lived in the Park, and laughing a lot, seeing those two oldies trying to keep up with you.

Wonderful mornings of sun and eucalyptus-fresh air!

You would get tired and when we arrived back at home for lunch you would be ready to sit down. After eating you would love to listen to a story about a family of rabbits with a patient mother.

A year is a long time for you. You have grown a lot and learned so many more words.

A year for us now goes very fast and we forget a lot. And, do you know darling, your grandparents are a little shorter!

Thank you for being Sadie, our lovely granddaughter. Happy Third Birthday!

Two big hugs and kisses.

From, your Grandmother.

Rose

To my mother-in-law, with love

Writing in this section was supported by Alex

One day at a time…

In some ways, I was pleased when my diagnosis of dementia was confirmed. I didn't know, and couldn't understand why I was having such problems, and so I was really quite pleased when I was told 'yes, you do have dementia' (or 'you *will* have dementia'!).

The children were very good; I mean they had to be told. I did find this difficult, and made sure that my husband was with me when we told them, because I knew we all had to be together to do it. It was something that had to be done. I didn't want to pretend nothing had happened. I can't see the point in that, because eventually I would have had to have 'not pretended', because I couldn't have physically maintained the pretence anymore!

I have good days and bad days. I'm still surviving! But I do find sometimes, it's difficult, particularly in the afternoons. Whether it's just because I'm tired, or something more than this I don't know, but I find the afternoons very difficult. At the moment it is certainly memory that is most affected by my dementia. I can still do many everyday tasks, such as cleaning the house, and talking to people on the phone, but it's remembering! For example today has been particularly bad. It's been one of those days where everything begins fine, and then it just hits me.

On the whole however, and considering what my husband and I are going through, I think most of the time, we are coping quite well. My husband has been superb, (and he always will be, I know), but there are times when I really don't know what I'm doing: *'Why am I here, what's happening?'* But we've got to keep going.

Luckily my daughters are very supportive, and even my grandchildren, (apart from the youngest, who can't take it in quite yet), know what's happening. In fact, we're seeing more of them than ever now, which is lovely. They could quite easily have said, 'Oh well, we'll see you a couple of times a year', but they haven't. I quite often have the grandchildren over, the eldest of whom is now twelve, and who still rings me up and asks 'nanny, when am I coming to see you again?' Obviously, they don't know everything that's happening, but they know nanny's not well, and it doesn't affect them at all.

I have found the Forget-Me-Nots have been very good. It is great to see people still doing lots of 'good things', interesting and worthwhile projects, despite our dementia. I realise that people are all going to be at different levels, and some days I'm fine and some days I'm not, so I understand this well!

I certainly still enjoy life, and my husband and I still do a lot together. On the whole (touch wood) we are coping. I'm still looking after the house; I enjoy doing our wonderful garden and our allotment, which takes up a large proportion of our time, but keeps us busy! I still love reading, which is important to me as I have always done a lot of reading, and if I could no longer read I would be thinking gosh, what do I do next! However, at the moment I am still reading everything I want to read. We also still enjoy walking together, particularly walks along the beach, which is very close to us.

When it comes to dementia, you just have to take it a day at a time.

This is a Kenning poem about our beloved rescue dog, a Labrador named Remus.

Remus

Wonderful-swimmer
Risk-taker
Alone-whiner
People-lover
Food-stealer
Company-keeper
Attention-seeker
Faithful be-friender

My Family and Other Animals

I was born just after the war in Rugby, Warwickshire. Although Warwickshire was not badly hit during the war, it was definitely tighten belts! There wasn't much money around. You had to be careful about eating the food. You couldn't waste anything, nothing at all.

I was an only-child. My mother had problems when I was a baby, and she never had any more children even though she would have liked to. In some respects I quite liked being the only child, because it was lovely just to have time with mum and dad, to do things with them and have time to myself. It would have been nice to have a brother and sister and do other things, but it was not to be.

Most of the time, I got on well with my parents; my dad better than my mum. My mum was the one that was determined that everybody would do exactly what she wanted them to do. You had to behave yourself!

With my mother, everything had to be just so. Everything had to be perfect. And she did love to cook for everybody. Everything was really really tidy for her. I would get into trouble if I would untidy things my mother had tidied up. I would be told to go away and sort it out!

My father worked very hard, and always had worked very hard. He was an electrician, and he travelled a lot, going from place to place carrying out checks and making sure things were being done properly and all the rest of it. My father didn't get home from work until 6 o'clock in the evenings, and when home he just needed to have a nice meal with his wife and myself, and then enjoy his free time relaxing.

My mum stayed at home as a housewife, which was just the way at the time. But we had a good life, considering that my parents didn't have a lot of money, I was made to feel that I was special. I was very lucky, I had lovely parents.

As a child, I remember playing with my Grandmother's old button box when I used to visit her. I used to love going to her house, she had a really old house, and she was lovely. She had the most beautiful garden. It was only a very long narrow garden, but it was absolutely fantastic. It was all her own doing, she loved gardening.

She always got loads of food, fed me up when I went round. Raspberries. She used to grow them in the garden, and strawberries as well. I used to help her pick them and she would make raspberry jam. She was well known for her raspberry jam! She also made her own bread every day, to eat with the jam: the smell in her kitchen was delicious! Loads and loads of food! It shows how different things are now, fewer people do this.

She was lovely. A very kind lady when you look back, she would always help other people. People would go to her if they had a problem, a bit of an agony aunt, but she was happy to do it. Funnily enough, my children then adored that button box. They were both tiny-tiny but they loved the button box. They would play with it for hours and hours and hours. And now when my granddaughter (who is now eight) comes to stay with me, she plays with the button box! The very same button box as my grandmother used to have that I played with all those years ago.

At school, we had quite a nice circle of friends. Not a lot of friends, but the ones I did have were a good circle, and we got on together well and did lots of things together. We all had separate desks at school, with all the boys on one side of the classroom, and all the girls on the other. We could get together, but only out of the classroom! In break times we could socialise with the boys if we wanted to spend our breaks running around with them. I think on the whole we didn't, so the girls stayed together. In those days we were quite shy and cautious of one another-not like it is today!

As we got older, we went out quite a lot as a group and enjoyed life, as most people do, but we knew our barriers, and what we could and couldn't get away with! So we wouldn't go too far.

My mother's sister had two sons much older than me. The boys started going to listen to all sorts of music at gigs, and very kindly took me with them. This was the beginning of my love for music.

We had a curfew by which time we had to get home in the evenings, and let's face it, in those days you always had to do what your mother told you to do, whereas nowadays it is rather different!

A Proposal

I only wear one ring now, and that is my wedding ring. I remember when Peter proposed. We went out for a meal, which we tended to do, and we were with another couple who we were very close with. This was, in fact, the couple that introduced us to each other, friends from the Navy.

They decided that we would go for this meal and it was so strange because they chose a really posh place, which we'd never done before, always favouring something cheap and cheerful. I thought something must be up!

And then Pete asked me to marry him!

He didn't get down on one knee, but it just surprised me that he did it in front of everybody. We were having a meal and he just said 'I want to marry you, will you let me marry you?' Then he produced the ring out of nowhere!

It was strange really, because he was away a lot of the time, as anyone in the Navy is. The worst was when he was away a year less a day, and that was hard. I was lucky as I had friends in the same situation, and we all got together and we made the most of it. All we had for near a year was letters to keep in touch. I didn't really think about keeping them, but we should have done. Then the children could have read what we were doing!

A Surprise

I was just getting my lunch ready when my husband, (who worked in the Navy), walked in the door. He sat down with me to say that he had been asked to go to Hong Kong! The man originally selected to go had fallen and broken his arm and leg, and would my husband like to go in his place?

My initial reaction was 'oh my goodness'. There I was, seven months pregnant with our first child and I thought *No, Not doing it.* But then I thought, *Well, if I don't do it I'll always regret it.* So we did it!

After talking with my husband, we decided that he would go to Hong Kong, and I would go to my mum's and follow after the baby was born.

I was in hospital for a long time before the baby decided to arrive. One day, I'd gone to a clinic for a check-up, to make sure everything was ok, as she was quite late, and they whooshed me off to hospital straight away and I was put in a bed! I stayed in hospital for three weeks, but it felt like three months!

I wasn't allowed to get out of bed, or do anything, because they thought the baby wasn't going to survive. I was stuck in bed for a long long time before the baby arrived. That was awful. And, of course, Pete was away, having just moved out to Hong Kong!

I was very worried. In hospital I got bigger and bigger and bigger.... I was supposed to eat, but I was finding it really difficult. It was hard, but we laugh about it now. When I came out of hospital I was huge! I'd been stuck in bed for so long and they stood over me and made sure that I ate and ate!

The funniest part was when someone came in one day, and walked past me, and I thought, *I know that face-who is it?* Then he turned around and looked at me, and he came running across, and it was my husband's brother! He said 'Did you realise my wife's in hospital?!' 'No,' I replied. Wasn't that funny, both of us in hospital, giving birth at the same time? Weird!

I didn't like being in hospital, it was dreadful. Couldn't move, couldn't do anything. I got fed up of reading books and magazines, and they didn't have televisions in those days. Just stuck there. But we got through it, and Pete did finally see his baby. It was about two months afterwards when I went out to Hong Kong. He met me from the plane and the expression on his face when he saw his baby daughter for the first time was magical. He rushed to see me, and then saw this little face and it was 'Look what I've got! What do I do with it!' It was a shock, but a lovely surprise.

The World I've Seen

The pace of life in Hong Kong was really busy and frenetic. Everything was fast and furious! The only place of peace and quiet that we ever found was round the back of the island; there was an area where nobody lived, with a beautiful beach, and you just took your swimming gear and it was wonderful. The rooms we had were superb - really high with fantastic views of the city. We were there for two years, and got to know people very easily and had great fun with everyone, including our new daughter! During our time there we had several holidays in China, and loved the people, as well as enjoying finding new places to go.

Whilst we were out there we asked my mother (who was a lovely lady, albeit not very well travelled), 'Would you like to come?' 'Oh no no, I can't do it, it's too much,' was the reply. I said 'It's entirely up to you, but if you want to, you can come.' And eventually she decided she would do it! She did it on her own, she came all the way to Hong Kong, and she thought it was wonderful.

She stayed with us for a month, and everyone made such a fuss of her, because at that time she was the only relative that had come out to visit. An added bonus was it meant she could look after my daughter for me, and I could go out! It was the first time she had ever been abroad, and I never dreamt she would come - but she did! She must have been amazed at the contrast of Hong Kong to Rugby, Warwickshire.

The two years went very quickly, and we were soon back in England. Two years later I had another girl, and life was really good.

One day, several years later my husband came home from work and said he had been asked to go to Brunei, and take us with him. Of course we said yes! Once you've done something like that, you get a taste for it. It makes you want to go around and explore, and we have been to so many countries now, and seen so much of the world, (both in our time abroad and subsequently on our travels), that we would never have seen, or ventured to if we had never gone to Hong Kong all those years ago.

In Brunei we had a wonderful time. School for the children was from 7am-12 o'clock. After that the time was ours for the rest of the day! We used to spend many afternoons relaxing and swimming in the swimming pool. The children wanted to stay - they enjoyed it so much. We were there for two years, loving every minute of it. We had a house to ourselves, a huge space to store everything in, it was wonderful. There were so many of us from the Navy out there, that we all had a really good time.

I did miss England, because we'd been in England for such a long time, but we really enjoyed where we were, and what we were doing! I was concerned about the children and moving them away to Brunei, one was four and one was eight when we first arrived, but they thoroughly enjoyed it.

We bought this plate in 1984, our first year there. Engraved on it is a mosque. They have a lot of mosques, and they are beautiful buildings, and we enjoyed so much visiting them and taking in their culture. To go to Asia in the 80s was very exotic; there were few people from England that had even been to

Brunei, let alone move there! Nowadays everybody goes abroad, but people didn't in those days, or at least not very often. Our friends thought we were absolutely mad. But if I hadn't gone with my husband I wouldn't have seen him for over a year! So for me there was no question. It was decided we've got to go, and that's it!

To keep in touch with our parents and family we had to write letters, you couldn't do anything else much in those days, it was just writing letters backwards and forwards. I didn't keep any of the letters which is so stupid really. I never even thought about it, I just thought, 'I've read that one,' and it went in the bin! But I thought afterwards, we should have kept them. The children would have appreciated them, but it was too late. It was lovely to come back and see family, because that was the bit I missed the most: family.

Brunei was lovely, very calm. We used to laugh in the evenings, because we would always go out after we had eaten a meal, and it was always men! There were no women out at all. It was always the men. The women were at home of course, but a lot of the men would go out in the evenings, and then they'd see me and the girls coming, and they'd all stand to one side! It was so lovely, they were so respectful but also absolutely amazed to see women out. They watched us wherever we went: we were a bit of a spectacle!

But you had to be very careful what you wore, you had to make sure you were covered up. You had to be careful not to upset anybody. They didn't insist that you covered everything up, but they insisted that if you went out after a meal, or just for a walk, you had to make sure that you were mostly covered, especially shoulders and legs. And why not? This was their culture and their beliefs, and led to me acquiring a huge sarong collection! Sarongs covered everything, and all of us wore them because we knew they were 'safe' and the colours were beautiful. Of course, because it was there and we could afford it, we brought a huge collection home with us!

The residents of Brunei were probably also not used to seeing many white women at the time, and it must have made a big difference to them, because the culture was very much that the women stayed at home all the time. The only time we ever saw the women was right at the beginning of the day, when they would go and buy the food for the day, and then we would never see them again. For us, it was really strange. Whether it is still like this today or not, I don't know. I imagine things will have changed quite a lot in the last thirty odd years.

Whilst we were out there we had a sailing boat. The guys were used to boats anyway, so we just sat there good as gold while letting them do all the hard work! We bought the boat ourselves while we were out there, we could afford to do it, then. It was lovely clear blue water. Once you had gone through the break, it was like being in a different world. The children were good, they were still fairly young, but they knew they had to behave themselves on the boat, and it was brilliant.

Once you come out of Brunei, there are several sets of islands close by, so we tried to work our way round them all. Every week we went somewhere. Sometimes we stayed near the island, other times we went off and explored something else.

We were out there for two and a half years, so we really got into it. We had one of those great big hampers we would take with us, so the food was there for all day, a huge picnic! It was just wonderful.

When we came back to the UK, we had a little boat, because we had enjoyed having the boat so much. We didn't keep it for very long though, because there were just too many other things to do; it became a bit much.

The children did really well, it gave them a lot of confidence. When they returned to school in England, we discovered they were ahead of the other children, and had to wait while the other children caught up! They hated it, but despite their protests they still went to school!

We loved being in both Hong Kong and Brunei, and learnt a lot from it. We were very lucky to have had such an amazing opportunity, and the children thrived.

They do make me laugh sometimes, because the children will suddenly say, 'Mummy, do you remember when we did so and so?' and I'm thinking, *I can't remember that!* There is so much I can't remember now. But they can tell me the stories!

When we first came home, the noise and busyness was so overwhelming. It was always so peaceful in Brunei, and suddenly we were in the midst of it all again, but we got used to it.

I don't know that I would go back to Brunei again; it's a long time now since we were there, and if we did go I would perhaps be disappointed. I don't know how it has changed, and I would rather leave it as it is in my memory. They were good memories and even the girls can remember - and it's amazing how much they remember, even though they were so young. My eldest daughter went off around the world after that with some friends, and it was, 'Bye, I'll see you in about two years' time!' They had a wonderful time, and why not?! That's what life's all about, isn't it?

Christmas

It was always the smell at Christmas, not only the food which was always there. It was the fact that the tree was there, and you had the smell of the pine needles.

We always used to go to church (because we had to go to church), and I had to behave myself.

My parents didn't have a lot of money so therefore even at Christmas we didn't get a lot. But we had to make the best of it. We had enough to have a tree and do a lovely meal, and all the family came and grandma came.

We had a lot of things that were home-made, or that were hand-me-downs. All my clothes used to come from other people, and go back to other people! Because that was just how we lived. But still I adored my mum, and one of my aunts was fantastic, too. So I was very lucky, because I had a lovely family.

I always have loved Christmas, and I still do! Every year I can't wait for it to be here. My children adore it too, because they've got children of their own.

Christmas to me was always very, very important. Don't know why, but it was. I loved doing everything towards Christmas, and I loved doing everything after it, too.

Because we were away a lot of the time, we did Christmas in different countries across the world. We still always got a roast dinner, though! In many ways, it was still very much like it would be in England, because most of the people there were English expats, but the weather was slightly hotter! I enjoyed every minute of it; it was lovely.

In our family, everyone comes together at Christmas. We have the grandchildren on one table, and us on another. It's quite crowded. I said to my husband a long time ago, 'the children are going to stop coming for Christmas, they've got children of their own and their own families!' But every year, they say, 'We're all coming to you mum, is that all right?'

Every year I'm thinking, *So many to fit it!* Of course, it gets very big... My husband does the cooking. I do the washing up; always have done, and always will do! My husband is more the cook out of the two of us. I do cook, obviously, because I have to - but he is the one that enjoys it, which is fine by me!

Here and Now

I think we have been very lucky because we have had a very good life. And now the children are more than old enough to look after themselves, they have given us some wonderful grandchildren and it's been brilliant. And the thing is they still want to come here!

Just recently I thought that my grandson would probably never want to come and stay with us again, because he's getting older, he's twelve now, and he phoned up the other day and said, 'Nanny, I haven't come to stay with you for a long time,' and I said, 'Well, you know you can come whenever you want to,' and he said 'Right - I'm coming tomorrow!' It's lovely to think that he still wants to come. And he brought his younger sister as well, she's eight. But they are as good as gold. We say 'Where do you want to go today, what do you want to do?' And they say 'Nothing, Nanny, we just want to stay here with you!!'

I think it is because they live a busy life anyway; they do a lot of things, school clubs and what have you, so to actually to come and stay with us for a couple of days is a nice change. My grandson is the one that makes me laugh, he is about a foot bigger than I am, huge, and he comes up to me, and I never dreamt that he would hug me by the age he is now, but he does. He's at 'big school' now, and has been for quite a while, but he's just amazing.

I find retirement lovely because we now have no responsibilities. We just do whatever we want, whenever we want to. It's been like that for a long time now. We fill our days with all sorts of things; we enjoy eating very much, we've always enjoyed eating! (I think most people do these days). We like to go off and find somewhere nice to eat. We don't go so much in the evenings, probably a lot of people do but I'd rather go at lunchtime because I find it's just a little bit easier. Otherwise you tend to think *Come on, we've got to hurry,* because you've got to be back for something, or someone else needs the table. I find it less time constraining, and more relaxing at lunchtime.

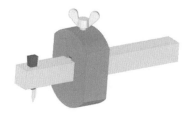

Tony

To my family

Writing in this section was supported by Alex

My Name

There was no question whatsoever that my mother was going to have a girl. All the time while she was carrying me I was Ann. And when I was born, stupidly it became Antony.

I don't like the name. I don't remember anybody calling me anything other than Tony.

When I did my carpentry apprenticeship at Thanet, one or two of the guys used to call me 'Ant'. The Antony hasn't got an H in it either. Anytime anybody said to me 'what's your name?' I would always reply 'Antony with no H'. Always had to say that. It was a pain being called that, really.

I think the disappointment to my mother at me not being a girl did not die off until she died, really! I have often wondered how far I would have got if I had been a girl...

Growing up in Wartime Kent

I was born in the tail end of 1939, just as the war started. We lived in Thanet, but there's nothing much in Thanet, except for the sea, which I loved as a child. However, when I was a young child you could not get to the sea; there were defences all-round the English coast during the war, with rolls of barbed wire on our beach. You simply couldn't get onto the sands! I suppose they thought if they put up a roll of barbed wire the Germans wouldn't get in. So there were no walks on the beach for me in my early days.

We lived within about a mile and a half of Manston airfield. That was a major RAF base at the time, as well as being a battle of Britain base, so it all happened at Manston.

Most children from our area (Westgate-On-Sea) were evacuated during the war. My little mate who I used to knock around with at the time was evacuated to Wales, and most of my other friends to places further inland, too. I suppose they thought they were safer.

My cousin and his parents, who lived across the road from us, moved to Pluckley for several years during the war, and we were supposed to have gone with them, but my mother wouldn't go.

My father worked on Manston airbase - not in the forces, but working for the maintenance team there, and, seeing as Manston was forever being bombed, he was forever putting up buildings again, and so my mother refused to go. She wanted to stay with him, and that meant I wasn't going anywhere either!

Looking back on it now, it wasn't a brilliant idea. If it had happened now, and it had been my children living within a mile and a half of an airfield that was suffering regular bombings, they'd have gone! The end result, as far as I was concerned at the time, was that I didn't have that many friends left to play with!

I can remember all around the Westgate area was full of bombsites, all over the place. All the Thanet towns suffered a lot of bomb damage. Whether they were aiming to hit the towns, or aiming for Manston airfield I'm not sure, but of course bombing was far less accurate then. I can remember so many bomb damaged properties near where I lived, and we used to play on the bomb sites. It wasn't anything that was unusual to us, the whole time I was a child they were always there, and we'd always had them: ready-made playgrounds.

We had a shelter in the garden, dug by my father, who was good at practically everything (including building air raid shelters!)

That place was magical to me. It was quite deep, with a mound over the top of it, and we were always playing down there as kids-even if there wasn't a raid on!

I remember the shelter was also multi-purpose: you could keep food down there, as you would in a fridge, because it was so cool. People just didn't have fridges at the time (including us), so we kept our butter, bacon, eggs and what have you down the shelter. We loved it down there as kids, and the shelter was still there when I left home, and when my mother moved out. Who knows, it may still be there today...

Holidays in Deal

A place I used to go to a lot growing up was Deal. It used to fascinate me because you could see the Goodwin Sands from there, which is a sandbank which is about a mile or so out to sea.

You were always getting boats wrecked on the sands. We used to go up there with our binoculars and see whether there were any new wrecks out on the sands. That was something I used to really look forward to, and thinking, *I haven't seen that one before!*

There was a wreck right up on the beach – quite a big boat. You would always think you could swim out to them, but really it was a bit too far. They have built a pier out there recently. The old pier as far as I know was a traditional old pier, but it got rammed by a boat in the 1920s or could have even been before then, and pretty well destroyed it. When I first knew Deal, there wasn't any pier whatsoever there, it had not been rebuilt yet. I don't know when they rebuilt it as the pier that is there today.

I used to love going to Deal because shingles was a novelty, where I lived in Thanet there was only sand! I used to love making the pebbles skim, and seeing how many times I could make it bounce: 'Cor, I made it bounce ten times,' I'd shout, (and if you believe that you'll believe anything!)

We used to stay in St Alfred's Square, and just up the road they had a bakery, and you only had to come out of our front door and you could smell the bread. I can almost smell and taste it now as I sit here. Every day we would be up the road for fresh rolls in the morning. I don't think they were actual relatives we stayed with, I think they were friends of my grandmother, but we termed them as relatives and had to give them a kiss like relatives!

A Place I Loved

A place I absolutely loved as a child was Sevenoaks, in Kent. I had relatives there; my aunt, uncle and cousin (who was a little older than me), and I used to go up there on holidays.

It was a very pretty place, and they lived by the Bradbourne Lakes, a web of ornamental lakes which were completely unbelievable to me as a kid. It had been part of a big estate many years previously, and in many, many years gone by, there was a big house there, and they created lakes out of a river that ran through the estate. The lakes were always full of ducks and swans and geese.

I couldn't wait to go there to play, and I had a lot of friends up there as well. A beautiful place. The countryside is really spectacular around there, and surprisingly close to London.

My cousin and I used to mess about on the lakes with boats, fishing nets and catching tiddlers. Whenever I have been anywhere near Sevenoaks, even up to fairly recently, I've also walked down and had a look at Bradbourne Lakes. It brings back so many memories of those holidays. And not only memories, I absolutely love the spot! Very beautiful and tranquil.

Normally my aunt used to take me up there, on the train as it was in those days, because so few people drove, or had cars. As a child I lived in a long road, at number 105 (of about 130 houses in the avenue we lived in), and I can remember there being two or three cars in the entire road, possibly half a dozen, but certainly no more than that. I visited again fairly recently, and of course it was no surprise to find all the front gardens had a car standing in them, plus cars parked nose to nose along the road!

I also spent many of my childhood days up in Knole Park, a picturesque place with a massive great old mansion (Knole House), and surrounded by many acres of beautiful countryside, open land and woodland. The highlight was the deer that roamed there, that in those days would come up to you because they'd know they were going to get something to eat!

Of course, we've been all over the place on holiday since then (both in England and abroad), and been to some lovely places. But Sevenoaks is the one that stays with me. A place that I have always loved, and always will do.

Please can I not go to Grandma's for Christmas?

My early childhood Christmases were looking through the Second World War. Quite sparse, I probably never had even one new toy up until the age of five or six because they were just not available.

My father was a carpenter so he used to make bits and pieces. I remember one big aeroplane I had that he made, I can see it now. Times then just weren't easy; there was just not much around, not for anyone.

For Christmas dinner we had a chicken. My grandfather on my father's side used to keep chickens and rabbits. I didn't know at the time, but I guess one would have been selected for the table.

My father had an allotment so we were alright for vegetables. I have a feeling allotments came about in the First World War, grow your own, etcetera.

We always used to go to one of my grandmother's for Christmas dinner, which I didn't enjoy that much.

From a very early age I was what I call 'dragged' over to my grandmother's, really against my will, when I'd sooner be at home playing with my toys. Instead of that, I was at my grandmother's, playing with nothing! I didn't really enjoy going over to that particular grandmother's. There was nothing wrong with her, it was just boring for a child.

We always had a Christmas tree, although heaven only knows where it came from. It used to appear, I think Santa used to bring it, down the chimney! (It is amazing it wasn't covered in soot...) I suppose that is the magic of Christmas!

After the war it took a long time for everything to be rebuilt. I guess Christmas presents got a bit better. I had a lot of Hornby train sets. The funny thing is where we lived we didn't have electricity. It was Victorian, and obviously built before electricity was put into houses, ordinary terraced houses at any rate. So I didn't have things like electric train sets, because they were pointless. The only thing I had was windup, clockwork stuff, and masses of Hornby.

We had an open fire in the back room, with a back boiler to heat water, but of course in the summer that was not alight, so we were all boiling kettles! It was just natural to us, bath times you had to light the fire! It seems archaic, doesn't it?

I can remember, particularly before we got electricity, the lamp in the ceiling of the back room we all lived in, with a yellow fringe shade, and what they called a bypass which meant there was a little tiny flame going all the time so we didn't have to get a match. They had mantles which were very, very delicate things. They were what gave you the light from the gas. The gas would come down a pipe into mantles which were made out of some sort of silk I think, and these mantles produced the light from the gas. That bypass was 'high tech' at the time. I can't imagine that now! But I can remember it. I am sure a lot of other places had electricity by then, but you see my parents didn't own the house.

Our next door neighbour who we used to call Aunty May,(she almost *was* my mother, she was always in the house), her brother owned the house. Then later, my grandfather died on my father's side, and my father inherited about two thousand quid (which was a small fortune), and he put electricity in. When we finally got electricity it must have been a shock!

Oh, to be an Archaeologist!

I was a carpenter by trade. Didn't really want to be a carpenter if I must be honest about it, but my father was a carpenter, his father was a carpenter and so forth, my father had his own building business so it was assumed I would go into that.

I really wanted to go into archaeology.

The reason for this was that I went to school in Canterbury, so I had to bus up and down from Thanet to Canterbury, and the whole top of the town in Canterbury was blitzed. Almost nothing there at all. When I first knew that part of Canterbury, by St George's Clock Tower, Marks & Spencers and our school were about the only things there! Well, part of our school was still there, but a lot of it was 'prefab buildings' which had been put up temporarily.

While I was there, in 1951, the government decided to lift the country out of its post-war depression and put on the Festival of Britain on the South Bank in London. A lot of towns and cities around the country followed suit. They had one in Canterbury, and they called it the Festival of Canterbury.

Our school was at the top of the city centre, and everywhere surrounding the school was completely blitzed. We used to walk to our school, and there were just basements full of weeds and Buddleia and all manner of things that grow in basements. So, in advance of the Festival of Canterbury, they cleared out a lot of the weeds to make way for the Festival site.

As they were clearing it out, we always used to go down

there as kids, and I became interested in what they were finding, and how they were going about excavating the site.

They were mostly finding everyday things that had been lost; the shop that sold fruit and veg, or hardware, or whatever it may be - all of a sudden was gone, and all the remnants left behind. Just watching these guys, a lot of whom I guess were students, digging around with their trowels, fascinated me.

I didn't pursue it because too seriously have a career in archaeology I would have needed to go to college or university, and in those days, my future was mapped out. It was a bit in those days. I was going to be a carpenter, and that was that.

I am certainly not sorry I was a carpenter, because I got an apprenticeship with a very good local builder.

What would my father have said if I had told him I wanted to do archaeology? 'You want to get a trade behind you, my son!' This to some extent in those days was true. You could leave school and work in a shop or something of the like, but if you actually had a trade, it was considered a good career, and something you could always fall back on.

Although, even after having got my trade in carpentry, if I had gone back to my father and said 'Now can I do archaeology?' he probably would have replied 'You've got a good trade, what do you want to go and do that for?!' He was a hands on sort of man; he didn't really understand. He was always into tools and building and woodwork, as I am!

I have a large workshop in my garden full of tools and wood that keeps me busy. I don't do so much out there now, but at one time I was always out there.

One of the joys of being in Canterbury therefore for me, ever since I was a child, is that it has so much history. Any time I walk through the town I can just spend hours looking. The buildings are so interesting and varied, both historic and modern.

I walk down the high street, and I'll never get tired at looking at the rooftops, especially in the older part of the city. It is a marvellous place to be.

The Marking Gauge

What this marking gauge means to me is a connection to my heritage.

It was used as an everyday tool by my ancestors, primarily my great grandfather, whose initials are engraved on it. It was so ordinary to him, something he would have picked up, held and used, and put down again every day. Nothing special. However to me, because of this, it holds great sentimental value.

A marking gauge was used to mark a straight line on wood, prior to sawing it. It is a tool which you can adjust, and the line on wood is made by a metal point, which you then cut (or saw) to. It's made of beech wood, and looks very well used-yet still functional.

I imagine my great grandfather would have used this probably in the 1870s, and the gauge itself could possibly even be older than that, because we don't know if it was bought new or second hand (with the initials engraved later).

The working face of the gauge has two brass inserts, and one of these is well worn with use. For some strange reason you always used them in your left hand, I can't really think why, now it comes to it, but we were always taught to use them in our left hand.

Not knowing my great grandfather, the person this tool reminds me of is my grandfather.

My grandfather only had the sight of one eye, and one eye was closed all the time. He used to hair about Westgate on a bicycle, and I am sure he couldn't see where he was going! He was the most peculiar sight, I should think.

He was obviously quite a clever man, and a very good carpenter, I know.

When he moved to Westgate he bought what then became known as 'Pinkney's Yard' on Belmont Road in Westgate-On-Sea, and there he had workshops, which you accessed from the Belmont Road. In between the workshops were a lot of lock up garages, and a big open garage.

Visitors used to use them in the summer a lot, especially the open garage. My father brought me down there, because they had to move cars about for people to get their car out. As quite a young lad, I was actually driving cars and moving them all about a bit. And that was Pinkney's Yard!

It's not there now, there are houses built there now. Originally the lock up garages were stables, (before motor vehicles were about), and I can remember a manger being there too, a remnant from those early days.

My grandfather would have used this marking gauge too, in the early 20th century. When you think he and my great grandfather actually got hold of this tool more than a hundred years ago, measured a distance and cut to it, to me that is something quite special.

Marking gauges are still used now, and my antique, (with a bit of tweaking), was of such good quality that it could still be used today.

The Thanet Music Scene

It was the 1960s, and I was on the committee of the Rendezvous club at Dreamland Ballroom, in Margate.

There were two dancehalls at Dreamland, both very popular with young people, and they used to attract a lot of famous people. We ran what they used to call the 'Rendezvous Club,' which was a Sunday night dance club.

Public Sunday night dancing was illegal in those days, and if you wanted to go dancing it had to be something private: by forming a club, it became private. We would register two, three, or four hundred people in a night, who of course then became 'members' of the club, so it was then legal.

I remember leaning against the side of coffee bar and chatting to Mick Jagger, watching a group called The Barron Knights, who were another popular group in those days. We had all the big music names of the time, that most people have forgotten about now. The Tremolos used to come down a lot, I knew them quite well. They made the big time eventually. I saw so many people who became stars, or celebrities, and thought nothing of it. It was just day to day life! I didn't think of getting autographs.

The Thanet music scene was very lively then; people used to come down from London sometimes to play and absorb the music scene. Those were the days! I never met the Beatles, which I was always rather sorry about. The Beatles did come down to Thanet but I never actually met them. But practically every other big group of the time (late '50s and '60s) I met!

I used to play as well. I played guitar in one or two of the pubs in Thanet. I played whatever was current at the time. I mainly leant towards country music, but when you look at the big stars of the time, Elvis Presley, Dolly Parton, Dusty Springfield, their style was basically country based.

A perk was that it also was quite popular with the girls: I used to DJ in dreamland a couple of nights a week as well. That could lead to anything! All the girls used to flock up on stage and the stories that followed - I'll keep for my memories only!

They were good times. I enjoyed playing, but I let it go for years and years. I have picked up a guitar since, but I can't do anything like I used to, and then it gets frustrating. You have to use it or lose it!

With it being a Sunday night dance club; it had to be non-profit making. All the money had to go back into the club. What we used to do was build up a few thousand as a club, and then put a free night on, and try and get a really good group on. I can honestly remember putting The Rolling Stones on for nothing. Mick Jagger was reasonably local, from Kent, and was often around.

I remember seeing The Rolling Stones for the first time on stage, and just thinking how scruffy they were! Groups at the time all wore suits, and then The Stones came on, and I thought *'They are never going to get anywhere!'* They had a scruffy, dirty look about them - but the girls went potty for them! *'They'll never get anywhere'*, that was my prediction - so never take any notice of

anything I predict!

The job that changed my life

I was already married at the time, not that happily married I must say: she didn't want children ever. That's a big decision, and it was something that hadn't sunk in for me at the time. I just thought, so what! But I shouldn't have married her; I knew I shouldn't have married her.

The other thing was she never really left home. I wouldn't like to blame her for that because it was possibly partly my fault as well, who knows? I only see my side of it.

We never bought anywhere together; we lived in a rented property down in Westgate-On-Sea. It wasn't a brilliant marriage. She was always, always, always at her mother's. It seemed to run in the family, because her mother was like that as well. Her mother's mother lived two doors away; she might as well have lived with her, honestly. Everybody flocked to Grandmother's. It wasn't ideal.

At that time I'd been involved in a motorcycle business, and we also used to do garden machinery, servicing them, so I was very well up with small engines, two stroke engines and things like that.

I saw an advert in the paper for Ricemans, in Canterbury (which later became Fenwicks). They'd got a gardening department and wanted to expand it considerably, and they wanted somebody who was well up on garden machinery and engines to do both selling and servicing, as they had workshops in Dover Street.

I went for the interview and it must have been the personnel manager, somebody else, and the third person sitting in on the interview (because he was well in with the Ricemans) was a guy called Graham Rainer, and he was chief buyer for menswear. I don't why he was at the interview, but I think he sat in on most interviews for staff there. He and Jonathan Riceman used to go drinking together.

They said to me, 'We'd like you to start, but we haven't quite got everything in place yet. If you'd like to get used to the company workings and everything, you can come and work on menswear for a month or so'. So I thought OK, although I wasn't interested in menswear, not at all. Having said that I am glad I did it, as I got well into retail. The whole experience turned out to be very interesting.

So I was working on menswear, and Hazel (now my wife) was one of two on the switchboard at Ricemans.

As part of Hazel's job, when the post came in she had to sort the letters out and bring them round to the departments. She used to walk into our department at least once a day.

Oh my God, she was so attractive! She really was. There was always a bit of a 'wink wink nudge nudge' between us lads. She had lovely brunette hair, she always got noticed. She used to walk in every day. When you are in a store like that with so many employees, you tend to sort of form cliques. You go to lunch and dinner together with the same people, who go at the same time as you, so you sit with them and what have you, and that is really how I got to know her. She was a stunner.

Eventually my marriage broke up, and I married Hazel, and then we had kids, and then grandchildren!

The car accident that changed my career

I had a Volkswagen Beetle. The nearest Volkswagen dealer in those days was in Sturry, and I was booked in for a job or a service or something.

A friend of mine had a bit of a haulage business and I used to drive for him sometimes, on an odd job basis. The night before I was due to take my car in for service; I had been to Southampton in his lorry!

I took the lorry there and back again, got an hour's kip on the settee, and set the alarm, got up and took my car to the garage in Sturry... and didn't make it. I got a mile from home and on the dual carriage way coming into Birchington, I went straight up the back of a steam roller! I must have just dozed off, there was no other reason for it. Car was in good nick, there was no reason other than I was tired, and I wasn't concentrating.

I banged myself up quite a lot. I thought I had lost my right eye. There is a bit of a scar there, it doesn't look much now but at the time when that bandage came off, I could see, oh boy, my poor looks! I was off work for a long time; I'd cracked a couple of ribs and all sorts of things.

I was going out with my now wife at the time, and I wasn't able to work for a long time. Hazel's mum was doing some fruit picking at a farm called Neil's Place. The guy who she was working for, who managed the farm, was ever such a nice bloke, and she must have been talking about me and the fact that I was getting better, and possibly could do something again and he said

'I could do with a hand up here!' He wanted someone who could drive the tractor and pick up all the bobkins full of fruit. I had never been on a tractor in my life but I gave it a go and I really loved it!

I really enjoyed being out and I was interested in all the trees and the fruit, they grew apples, pears, a little soft fruit like raspberries, gooseberries. Mostly apples and pears. There were some plums but they had let them go. I absolutely loved it. The owner had only just bought the place, it used to belong to Mounts, who were one of the big fruit growers in the area, and it was one of their old farms, all their old trees, seventy or eighty years old perhaps.

The guy who bought it said he wanted to completely grub everything out and replant it. So when the fruit picking was done, Peter, the manager there, who I was working for, said would I like to stay and help him with this? So I stayed on there and we grubbed all the old trees out and planted loads of new stuff: I expect some of my planting is still up there!

I liked it so much, but I couldn't go anywhere there - it was a very small place. Then I saw an advert for fruit growing at Chartham Hatch, with a big fruit grower.

I went for it and they sent me on courses and all sorts. I got well into it and really, really enjoyed it. Eventually I went out on my own, self-employed as a contractor, pruning mostly.

At fruit picking time I would go and find a job driving, mostly, or running a gang of fruit pickers. It is quite a demanding, busy job running a gang of 15 to 20 fruit pickers because you have to get what you are picking absolutely right, because what you're picking goes into store. It could be put away in September and might come out in February, March time, so it has to be pretty good. You don't want to store a load of rubbish and then chuck half of it away!

We also used to prune in the summer, but for different reasons. Most of my year was spent pruning, except in the picking season. Sometimes I would take a holiday for two or three weeks in the picking season, sometimes I would get a job running fruit picking gangs.

I was in this business for many years, and I more or else ended my working life with fruit! That is what I enjoyed doing, out in the fresh air. The one thing I didn't like was rain, and I still don't like it. It is just one of those things that if you are going to a job like that, you have to accept that, sometimes, you are going to get wet!

I didn't really have a set date when I would retire; I sort of wound it down really in my sixties. Not sure when I actually stopped. I was a carpenter by trade, and I was always interested in antiques, so then I did a course at one of the colleges in Canterbury in antique restoration. I still do the odd bit, but not too much nowadays.

The teacher was an absolutely brilliant restorer. He was based at Deal, and I used to go out there quite often, and he gave me work. I really enjoyed doing that and I still do really, I still do bits and pieces. Hazel does a few boot fairs during the year and if I do something up I sell them through that. By and large I don't make a lot, but I enjoy doing it.

A Place Where I Was Happy

I have never been any happier than being here, where I am now, in my house in Rough Common, on the outskirts of Canterbury. I love being here. I love being outdoors, and I'll never get tired of the view from my garden, looking down the hill over Canterbury and the surrounding countryside.

Of course, it changes from season to season. You see the trees change colour, and come autumn the line of trees my garden overlooks turns a shade of golden, which is just beautiful. Unfortunately, this also signs the onset of winter and the beginning of (often) non-stop, pouring rain!

From my upstairs windows you can also see Canterbury Cathedral, which although still a stunning view by day, is even more so by night, when the cathedral is illuminated as well. A beautiful sight. When my American relatives come to visit, the first thing they want to do is get out in that garden and look at the view. 'What would we give to live here!' they say, and coming from the deep south of Texas, (where they will often drive for hours and see nothing), I quite agree with them.

I have lived in this house for ten years now. It originally belonged to my in-laws, who bought it new, off-plan, without even seeing it! They lived in Watford, and wanted to come down to Kent ready for a quiet retirement. My wife's sister and her husband were already down here as he worked for a local timber company. His company were supplying the timber for these houses, so naturally he got wind of the new houses long before many other people got to know of their existence! He was straight on the phone to my in-laws, 'You want to come and see this site!' My father-in-law came down, and thought yes, this would suit me fine! And he had his pick of the plots, the best one of which he bought before they'd even started building them.

I love it here, especially when we have animals in the field just beyond my garden. Sheep, mostly, although we have had pretty well all farmyard animals over the ten years. When I first knew the house, there were always pigs out here, giving rise to the field being known as 'the pig field'. They were smashing. They used to come up to fence and let you scratch their heads. Of course, all the houses that backed onto the field used to chuck titbits over for them, which meant they used to get quite friendly to us, and it was lovely having them here.

The field was owned by butchers at the time, so unfortunately the pigs never stayed long!

Dementia

Dementia. The only difference for me really, is my memory. I can't think there is any other difference - but then, maybe that's the dementia!

I can remember things from way back (you know, 1760, when I was quite young!) However more recent things, I can't remember.

It's not all the time, and it's not terrible- there is nothing terrible about it. I just tend to forget things! Everybody forgets things, but I forget more than maybe you, the reader at home would.

When I got given the diagnosis, I was shocked. In fact shocked is not the word! That particular word - dementia - to me has a terrible sound about it: demented. *Demented.*

For someone to say to me 'You have dementia' to me implied 'you are demented!' That wasn't at all nice. If it is somebody who is obviously used to talking about it and using the word, like social workers, doctors, then that is just a word that they use! But for me receiving it, it was not the same at all. It was upsetting.

I didn't find it hard to speak to my family and tell them; they possibly had noticed my memory was getting worse, so perhaps it was not a massive shock to them.

They have been supportive, but I don't think they have had to support me much more since I got the diagnosis, life has just carried on as far as I can see.

I have a write-on calendar which I always use to write

anything important on, that helps my memory a lot. I don't really have a routine, other than I love walking the dog every morning, and I go to Folkestone to see my daughter every Tuesday. Apart from that, the day comes and goes as it will. I spend a little time in the garage where I have a workshop, go into Canterbury, do the shopping. Indeed, these are activities I enjoy, regardless of dementia or not.

Since I got the diagnosis, I think I am the same person.

I don't think my personality has changed, although other people might be the judge of that. The only thing that has changed (as far as I am aware) is my memory has got worse. But again, it is important to stress that it is not terrible. With the aid of my calendar, and my family, I can manage it. I have the Forget-Me-Nots who indeed are a good support.

I get more out of my family than anything, and my dog. My eldest daughter works in Essex, and is very busy working in retail, and seldom around. So, although I live with my eldest, I don't really see much of her. I see more of my youngest who lives in Folkestone, more than any of them.

I know I am certainly not going to get better, but I don't feel as if I am getting worse. It doesn't seem that way to me. If I am, it is very, very slow.

I don't fear for the future. I don't think there is anything I can't do now, that I could do ten years ago! Driving is the one change of course, but generally speaking I don't miss it. Only very occasionally do I miss driving. I have always driven a small Vauxhall Astra van, and sometimes I will think, 'I wish had my van with me,' but not very often. My licence came up for renewal, and I had to have a driving test and I just thought, *I cannot be bothered!* I think for me, it was the right decision.

There is a bus stop just up the road from me, I walk up to the bus stop and enjoy that. It's something to do.

I like travelling on the bus, you see things you never realised were there when you were driving (especially from the top deck!) and meet people you would never usually meet otherwise. It's a novelty in a way, having spent so many years without going on buses at all! I find it is far more relaxing, travelling by bus.

I tend to read. I don't have the problem of forgetting what I've read so far, as a lot of what I read is factual, or autobiographical; I don't read a lot of fiction. I am just sorting some books out now. I have a very large collection, which I am trying to cut down. If I read all of them I'd probably need to live to be 160!

For me, a relaxed, easy going approach is absolutely the best way to tackle dementia. There is no use getting het-up about it; it's there! And if anybody asks me, 'Do you feel as if you've got dementia?' I say no!

The Maidstone Conference
A speech delivered by Chris N, Keith and M. J. Saints

Keith

Having spoken at conferences from the perspective of a person with dementia, I think it is important that each of us will first give you a sense of who we are as people, before briefly describing our dementia experience and then our engagement and empowerment through our Forget Me Not network in East Kent.

My name is Keith Oliver. I am married, with three grown up children and three grandchildren, and have lived in the Canterbury area for thirty three years. Until April 1st 2011, I was head teacher of a very large primary school, was studying for an MA, and was advising other Canterbury schools on behalf of Kent County Council. All that stopped with my diagnosis of Alzheimer's Disease at the age of fifty-five.

After devoting five months to my dementia assessment, and then five more months to come to terms with that, I decided that I needed to continue to try and play a useful role in society ad utilise some of the skills which, although waning a little, were still available to me, in order to raise awareness about what living well with dementia is really like.

Quickly, I was offered a voluntary role of 'Dementia Envoy,' within the Kent and Medway NHS Social Partnership Trust, and then I became a very busy person. Soon, I felt a greater impact could be had if others shared carrying the baton with me. Consequently in November 2012, six people with dementia and two clinical psychologists met to form what professionals called a 'Dementia Service User Network,' but which we insisted should be titled the 'Forget-Me-Nots.'

The group has grown to involve eighteen people with dementia, with support from six Kent University students on placement with the Trust, and our monthly meetings are co-chaired by two clinical psychologists and myself.

The function of the group is partly social comradeship and partly to be a useful resource to the NHS Trust in the area. The meetings last two hours and are a mix of structure to allow everyone with dementia the opportunity to contribute to the business, and informal during the break times. Both M.J. Saints and Chris N will talk about some of our projects, but four regular elements within our commitment are - being on interview panels for posts connected to dementia care, where we bring a unique perspective and assessment on the candidate, not as a professional, but as a person; we analyse and comment upon dementia related literature being generated by the NHS (the good, the bad and - yes, at times - the ugly documents), the British Psychology Society and other agencies prior to publication; we have participated in a number of worthwhile projects with DEEP and are active supporters of this very important venture; we speak at conferences and at post-diagnosis groups where often people in the audience have not long been diagnosed and are coming to terms with this and welcome hearing our experience and positive advice.

Last week I spoke at the Dementia Market Place event in

Canterbury, and wrote the talk the day that my mother had died - she had Alzheimer's, as well.

The group is attracting a lot of attention within Kent, the UK and beyond, and is consequently being increasingly called upon. I was delighted to recently announce at the launch of Kent's Dementia Action Alliance, as part of our Dementia Friendly Community initiative, that a West Kent satellite has been set up, based here in Maidstone.

I would now like to hand over to M. J. Saints, my fellow Forget-Me-Not...

M. J. Saints

Good afternoon. Today is the 14th of May, 2014.

We are in Maidstone, Kent.

Our Prime Minister is David Cameron, and the Leader of the Opposition is Edward Milliband.

After having given these answers to several GPs over a couple of years, a very kind locum listened to me when I said that I was having problems with memory, especially relating to language. She sent me to the Sarre Memory Clinic at the Queen Elizabeth Hospital in Margate. I'm very thankful to her!

At this clinic I was given various tests and a brain scan. In May 2012, I was diagnosed with vascular dementia. The clinical psychologist who gave me the tests was excellent and very supportive during this process.

After that, I went to meetings in Whitstable with a group of people with the same disease, but found it very difficult as the ladies running it weren't trained. It was the same psychologist who helped me originally, who suggested that I joined the Forget-Me-Nots, which I have been going to for about a year.

In this group, I have found a friendly atmosphere among people in the same situation as I am, and unlike other groups, it is run by people specifically trained to work with dementia sufferers. During this time, my experience has been very positive.

As a group, we have helped with the wording of papers and leaflets, having in mind the point of view of someone with dementia. We have also been involved with the British Psychological Society, sharing our views on the process of getting a diagnosis and the care (or lack of), that we have received. We have also been visited by two members of the House of Lords, who listened to our views which were used to help in the revision of the Mental Capacity Act.

The Forget-Me-Nots has given me hope, support and a sense of security in facing the future.

Thank you for listening. I will now hand over to my friend, Chris Norris

Chris N

I have been told that the art of a good talk is to use Brevity. I'll be covering this in much greater depth on page thirty five of my speech!

Hi, my name is Chris. I am married with two grown-up children and live in Ashford, Kent. I will be sixty in three days' time. Please excuse me reading from my notes.

I was diagnosed with fronto-temporal dementia eighteen months ago, which caused me to have to retire from work.

In my working life, I have been a Musician in H.M. Life Guards Mounted Band, where I was a State Trumpeter and played saxophone. I had to be able to play both these instruments while mounted on a horse. Not easy to do, as I had to steer the horse with my knees, both hands were needed to play the Saxophone!

Next, I was a village policeman in the Kent Police and, on my retirement, I became a driving instructor. I finished off my working life as a driving examiner for cars, tractors and taxis.

All these jobs required a very organised regime and I have always been a meticulous and methodical person. The onset of the fronto-temporal dementia hit me very hard as life became increasingly difficult due to my executive functioning being affected. Now it is very difficult for me to put things in a correct sequence, even down to the correct order of the letters in the alphabet, which is something learnt at an early age.

I am very involved in music making and most weekends I can be found on a Bandstand somewhere in Kent, or further afield. It has become increasingly difficult to read the music correctly and, like words, it is now harder to get the information off the page in the correct order and sequence. This overall effect that my fronto-temporal dementia has on me can be summed up in the famous Morecombe and Wise sketch with Andre Previn, where Eric Morecombe said 'I'm playing all the right notes but not necessarily in the right order!'

I have done two courses of cognitive stimulation therapy. The first was in a group (We called ourselves the Happy Wanderers, which was quite apt) and the second course was on a one-to-one basis.

On conclusion of the cognitive stimulation therapy in April this year, I joined the Forget-Me-Nots Group where I'm very much the 'newbie'. In order of time within the Forget-Me-Nots Group, the three of us on stage today are very much like the Three Bears. Keith is Papa Bear, M. J. Saints is Mamma Bear and I am Baby Bear. Goldilocks is working the slide presentation!

I have found being part of the Forget-Me-Nots Group very stimulating where it is good to exchange thoughts and views with my peers on numerous subjects surrounding dementia and coping mechanisms. Since joining the group in April, I have been involved in four projects and there will be two more before the end of the month. The group certainly gets us out and about!

One of the group's recent projects, which started in April, is a Life Writing Group. This is a Unique project in the United Kingdom which is being funded by DEEP (Dementia Engagement and Empowerment Project). We meet at The Beaney House of Art and Knowledge in Canterbury, a venue which is being provided free by the Kent County Council.

The Life Writing Group is a six session course which is a fun and easy way of celebrating our life experiences, both past and present. The aim is to record them in an enjoyable way for the participants and for others to then later share. The idea is to publish them, the publishing costs being funded by the Alzheimer's Society. The course is being supported and led by the author, Liz Jennings. There are about ten of us taking part and we are greatly supported and aided, almost on a one-to-one basis, by psychology students. They also help out at the main Forget-Me-Nots Meetings, so they are no strangers to us. At each session, we record these experiences by use of poetry and prose and we have already had two extremely enjoyable sessions.

Subject matters that we are investigating over the six sessions are :-

There's Nobody Like You

My Family and Other Animals

Life Changing Moments

The World I've Seen

Red Carpet Occasions, and

My Favourite Things

As with the main Forget-Me-Nots Group, I find this very stimulating and the feeling of friendship and community goes a long way to reassure all our group members that they are not alone in the strange and, sometimes confusing world of dementia.

Thank you for your interest and attention today and I will now hand you back to the capable hands of my fellow speaker, Keith Oliver.

Keith

We hope that has given you a sense of some of the achievements by Kent Forget-Me-Nots, the group of people with dementia who we have spoken on behalf of today.

We are closely allied to the aims and aspirations of the DEEP network, many of which we have outlined today with Steve Milton.

I am reminded of two stories - one around my weekly visits to a local primary school to hear children read. Lewis, who is nine, recently said to me, 'I saw you in a magazine at my Doctor's!'

He was right, as my story had been covered in a NHS magazine in Kent, and I quite expected to become involved in a deep conversation with this bright lad about living with dementia, so I answered, 'Did you, Lewis?'

He smiled, and said 'Yes, and I know your first name!'

Clearly the article about not being defined by one's dementia worked on this occasion!

The second story comes from 'Along The Way,' the joint autobiography of actor Martin Sheen and his son, Emilio Estevez. I have a enormous respect for Martin Sheen, as both an actor and a man, and this story is one which I often use in my talks to illustrate how I feel about speaking publicly about living well with dementia:

The Irish tell the story of a man who arrives at the gates of heaven and asks to be let in. 'Of course,' Saint Peter says, 'Just show me your scars.'

'I have no scars,' the man replies.

'What a pity,' Saint Peter says. 'Was there nothing worth fighting for?'

I hope that you agree with the sentiment that everything the three of us have shared with you today is worth fighting for, despite the occasional scars.

At our meeting last week, we talked about people who have inspired us. The doctor/clinical psychologist who shares the chair with me, without hesitation said that it is the members of this group who inspire her. I hope that what we've shared with your today will inspire you.

Thank you.

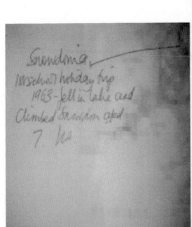

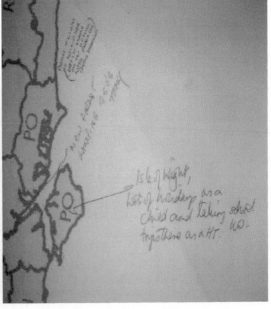

After the course...
by Liz Jennings

As a group, we've spoken about the legacy of this collection: as ever, these writers yearn for greater impact than their own personal pleasure or satisfaction. They long for others to live well, as they are trying to do.

I think there's a lot to be said for writing for personal pleasure and satisfaction: it does you a lot of good. Just last night, I was troubled by something that had happened in the day, and, at midnight, gave up trying to sleep and came to sit at the kitchen table and pour all my thoughts onto paper, knowing that rest would follow the release.

How about you? You have your own stories - and if you don't tell them, how will your loved ones hear them?

The great thing about life writing is that there's no right or wrong, simply your version of events, as you remember experiencing it. It's your chance to tell your side of the story.

With this in mind, we thought it would be nice to end the book with a few writing exercises that you are welcome to try. To get the most out of them, I'd really recommend doing them in company, and then sharing your results - something magical happens when you share your writing with others, taking the time to listen to each other and grow in understanding one another.

We hope you'll enjoy them, and we wish you every success as you, like us, seek to live well, whatever life throws at you.

Exercise 1: The First Time...

Set yourself a kitchen timer, and write for seven minutes on one of the following firsts:

- First pair of shoes
- First day at big school
- First time on a boat
- First dance
- First kiss
- First day at work

Exercise 2: Capture A Moment

At the top of a blank page, write the words 'I'll never forget the time I ...'

Set a kitchen timer again, just for five minutes this time, and continue the sentence.

Exercise 3: Something Special

Choose an object that's really special to you - and write about it with your trusty kitchen timer set for three minutes.

Exercise 4: Photo Finish

Choose a photograph from an album you have at home. Spend a couple of minutes really looking at it, and jot down thoughts that come to mind as you do.

You might like to list your thoughts in a particular order, and create a poem, or, alternatively, get that kitchen timer back out again and write for five minutes about the photo you've chosen. What senses does it reignite? Are there smells, sounds, or physical sensations that come to mind as you look at it?

Exercise 5: Put yourself on the map

At the end of this book, you'll have noticed photos of maps with handwriting on. These are from our fourth session, 'The World I've Seen.'

If you'd like to create your own life-map, I discovered you can find some very reasonably priced ones at a high street discount stationer's store! Lay the map out, and then write all over it - anything at all that comes to mind - with arrows pointing to the locations where your memories took place.

You might enjoy doing the exercise with others, over a cup of something nice, and sharing some of your experiences from around the world in the process.

Happy writing!

If you've enjoyed the writers' works contained in this collection, and would like to read more, search for the Forget-Me-Nots on Amazon where we have a volume of additional writings, *Life Goes On,* which is available to download for free.

Useful Web Addresses:

Alzheimer's Society UK

www.alzheimers.org.uk

DEEP Dementia Engagement and Empowerment Project

http://dementiavoices.org.uk/

Kent and Medway NHS Social Care Partnership Trust

www.kmpt.nhs.uk

Friends for Mental Health (East Kent)

www.kmpt.nhs.uk/friends-for-mental-health.htm

Liz Jennings

http://lizjenningscreative.weebly.com/

Christ Church University Adult Education Courses

http://www.canterbury.ac.uk/cae